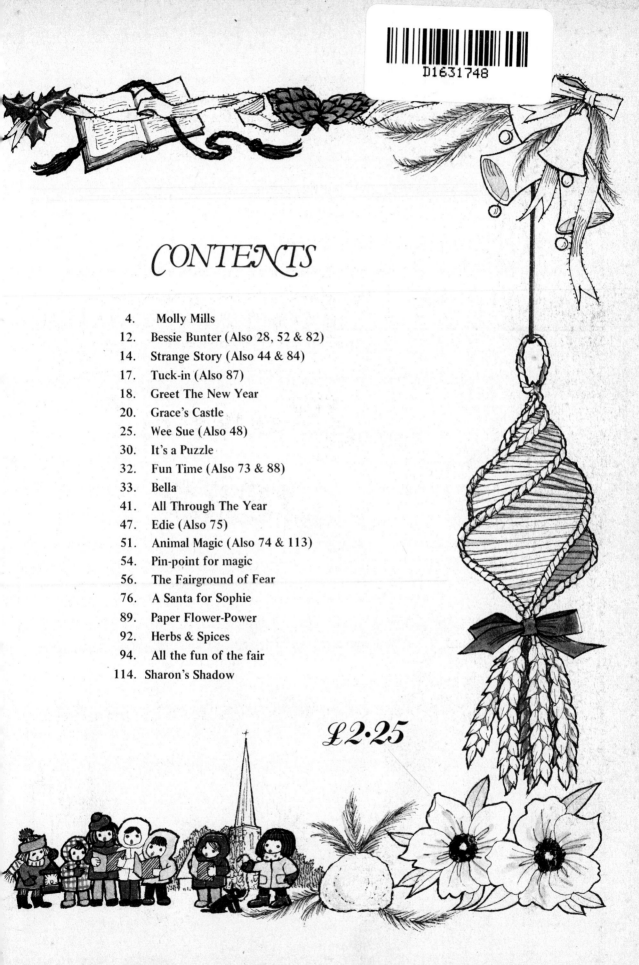

CONTENTS

£2·25

Molly Mills

It was nearly Christmas at Stanton Hall in Devon, where Molly Mills worked as a servant in the late 1920's...

THE FIRST SNOW OF THE SEASON, BETTY! MAKES EVERYTHING REAL CHRISTMASSY, DON'T IT?

BRR, **AND** COLD! LET'S EMPTY THESE BUCKETS AND GET BACK INDOORS!

YOU'VE ASKED FOR IT, CHARLIE BOY!

YAH! MISSED ME, MOLLY!

PERHAPS THIS'LL WARM YOU UP! HO, HO!

CHARLIE! YOU SNEAKY IMP!

But in the Servants' Hall, the bad-tempered butler, Pickering, was not amused...

Soon, a snowball fight was in full swing...

NOT LIKELY! YOU'RE ONLY GIRLS!

BETTER CRY OFF, CHARLIE, YOU'RE OUTNUMBERED TWO TO ONE!

PAH! I'LL SOON PUT A STOP TO THAT NONSENSE, COOK!

IT'S ONLY A BIT OF HARMLESS FUN, MR PICKERING.

5

THEY'RE ALL BIG STRONG LADS, 'CEPT HARRY HERE, WHO KEEPS THE ACCOUNTS! PERHAPS YOUR MASTER WOULD LET US CLEAR YOUR SNOW AND HELP OUR CAUSE!

HMM... LORD STANTON MIGHT HAVE, BUT HE'S NOT HERE. I CAN'T SEE THE BUTLER EVEN GIVING YOU THE TIME OF DAY!

OH WELL, IT'S WORTH A TRY! WE DO NEED EVERY PENNY WE CAN RAISE — AND THEN SOME MORE!

But...

CERTAINLY NOT! WHAT DO YOU THINK WE EMPLOY STAFF FOR? BE OFF WITH YOU!

HE REMINDS ME OF THAT BLOKE "SCROOGE" IN THE STORY!

'CEPT I CAN'T SEE MR PICKERING EVER TURNING OVER A NEW LEAF!

I SUPPPOSE YOU ENCOURAGED THOSE SCROUNGERS, MILLS?

IT'S ALL IN A GOOD CAUSE, MR PICKERING. I WISH WE COULD DO SOMETHING TO HELP GIVE POOR KIDS A HAPPY CHRISTMAS.

YOUR HEART'S AS SOFT AS YOUR HEAD, GIRL! I SUPPOSE YOU'D HAVE US GOING ROUND SINGING CAROLS, TOO!

HEY, IT MIGHT BE AN IDEA AT THAT! I WONDER...?

Molly hadn't been working long when Lord Stanton returned to the Hall from an early morning canter...

'MORNING, ME LORD.

SNOW CLEARING'S NO JOB FOR A GIRL, MOLLY, GET BACK INSIDE AND WARM YOURSELF UP! AS A MATTER OF FACT, I JUST MET A PARTY OF FELLOWS AND ASKED THEM TO COME ALONG HERE AND DO IT.

7

8

10

BESSIE BUNTER

Whispers in the Wind

A HIGH WIND, HOWLING AND GROANING THROUGH TREES, CAN ALWAYS SET THE SCENE FOR A STRANGE STORY. FOR WENDY PRICE, THE WIND WAS TO BECOME MORE THAN JUST A PART IN A STORY.

THE STRANGE STORY

PHEW, WHAT A WIND — I'M GLAD I'M NOT AT SEA JUST NOW!

YOU'LL FEEL BETTER ONCE WE'RE SETTLED IN AT OUR SUITE, WENDY. THE GEORGE IS THE MOST MODERN AND COMFORTABLE HOTEL IN TOWN!

WOW, WHAT A FANTASTIC SUITE, AND THIS PLANT IS PRETTY!

JUST ONE THING — IT FEELS SO COLD IN HERE. ICY COLD!

BUT LOOK—THIS PLANT'S SHRIVELLED UP WITH COLD, AND I HAVEN'T BEEN IN THE ROOM FIVE MINUTES!

CAN'T SAY AS I NOTICE IT, MISS. THE HOTEL IS FULLY CENTRAL HEATED!

IT WAS PROBABLY STARTING TO WITHER BEFORE YOU PICKED IT UP, MISS. STILL, I'LL GET AN ELECTRIC FIRE SENT UP IF YOU NEED ONE.

PLANTS DON'T USUALLY DIE SO QUICKLY. TH-THERE'S SOMETHING EERIE ABOUT IT

That evening . . .

HOW'S YOUR ROOM, DAD? MINE SEEMS SO MUCH COLDER THAN THE REST OF THE HOTEL.

SOME OF THE TOP ROOMS ARE BOUND TO GET CHILLY WHEN THE WIND'S BLOWING. I EXPECT SOMEONE LEFT A WINDOW OPEN. THAT'S ALL.

It took Wendy a long while to get to sleep that night. . .

THE COLDNESS SEEMS TO COME FROM INSIDE THE ROOM ITSELF, AND EVEN AN OPEN WINDOW WOULDN'T MAKE A PLANT DIE IN SECONDS. IT'S ALL VERY STRANGE.

In the middle of the night . . .

W—WHAT'S THAT? OH, IT—IT'S ONLY THE DOOR BEING BLOWN OPEN BY THE WIND! BUT THAT SOUND.

LIKE A GIRL, CRYING!

TH—THE ROOM'S EMPTY. YET I COULD HAVE SWORN—

DID YOU WANT SOMETHING, MISS? YOU RANG THE BELL FOR ROOM SERVICE.

EH? OH, I MUST HAVE PRESSED THE BUTTON BY ACCIDENT. I—I HEARD A GIRL CRYING, IN THIS ROOM.

IT'S TWO O'CLOCK IN THE MORNING, AND ALL OUR OTHER GUESTS ARE FAST ASLEEP. YOU MUST'VE BEEN DREAMING, MISS.

THE WIND CAN SOUND LIKE SOMEBODY CRYING, Y'KNOW. BUT IF THERE'S NOTHING YOU WANT, I'LL BID YOU GOOD-NIGHT.

I WISH I COULD BELIEVE THAT IT WAS ONLY THE WIND. NO, I'M BEING SILLY!

Next morning . . .

NO GOOD TELLING ME IT WAS A NIGHTMARE, DAD, IT SEEMED SO REAL!

STREWTH, THE WIND'S GETTING STRONGER! I'D BEST LEAVE YOU HERE AND DO MY BUSINESS CALLS BEFORE THE STORM BREAKS. YOU'LL BE OKAY, WON'T YOU?

YES, DAD, DON'T WORRY.

As the hours went by, the weather grew steadily worse . . . .

THE WIND'S REALLY HOWLING. I HOPE DAD ISN'T GOING TO BE AWAY MUCH LONGER!

And then, there came a sound of tapping . . .

I—I'M SURE THERE'S SOMEONE IN THE OTHER ROOM, KNOCKING AT THE DOOR. I—I CAN FEEL MYSELF TREMBLING ALL OVER, B—BUT I'VE GOT TO OPEN IT.

IT MUST'VE BEEN THE WIND BLOWING THOSE BRANCHES AGAINST THE WINDOW. HEY — THERE'S A GIRL IN THE GROUNDS, SOAKED TO THE SKIN. I—I'M GOING DOWN TO HER.

Wendy hurried down the stairs . . .

THERE'S THAT SOBBING AGAIN — LIKE I HEARD LAST NIGHT!

LET ME IN. PLEASE, LET ME IN.

THE GIRL SOUNDS ALMOST TOO WEAK TO CALL OUT ANY MORE. SHE'S PROBABLY BEEN BANGING ON THE BACK DOOR FOR AGES WITHOUT BEING HEARD AGAINST THE WIND AND STORM, POOR THING.

WHERE ARE YOU? I'VE OPENED THE DOOR!

PERHAPS SHE'S GONE TO THE FRONT ENTRANCE. THE RAIN'S PELTING AGAINST MY FACE — I CAN HARDLY SEE. AND I'M COLD, SO BITTERLY COLD.

Suddenly, in the darkness, there was a creak, and a loud roaring sound . . .

And when she opened her eyes again . . .

FEELING BETTER, WENDY? I'VE SOMETHING INTERESTING TO TELL YOU!

I WAS TALKING TO A CLIENT — HE TOLD ME THIS HOTEL WAS ONCE A LARGE HOUSE. A MAID HERE WAS ACCUSED OF STEALING A NECKLACE FROM HER MISTRESS AND SENT AWAY WITHOUT A PENNY. SHE WAS FOUND LATER, DEAD FROM COLD, HUNGER AND EXHAUSTION.

AND TODAY, WHEN THAT TREE FELL DOWN, A VERY OLD JACKDAW'S NEST WAS DISLODGED. THIS WAS FOUND INSIDE IT!

SO THE POOR GIRL WAS INNOCENT!

DAD, D–DIDN'T THE MAIDS ALWAYS SLEEP IN THE TOP ROOMS, UP NEAR THE ROOF, IN VICTORIAN TIMES?

YES, WENDY, THEY DID, AND PERHAPS THIS WAS HER ROOM. IT'S TAKEN A LONG TIME, BUT HER NAME'S BEEN CLEARED AT LAST.

THIS ROOM'S DIFFERENT NOW — IT'S WARMER AND THE FLOWERS ARE BLOOMING. EVEN THE SUN'S COME OUT. IT'S AS THOUGH SOME VEIL OF UNHAPPINESS HAS BEEN LIFTED AND WE CAN BE HAPPY AGAIN!

TUCK-IN with Tammy
CHEESE STRAWS

1

100g. plain flour.
50g. margarine.
50g. cheese.
Pinch of salt.
Pinch of pepper.
Cold water,
teaspoon, grater bowl,
baking sheet, wire tray,
rolling pin, dish, blunt
knife.

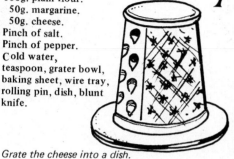

Grate the cheese into a dish.

2

Put the flour and margarine into a bowl and mix with your fingers until it forms little crumbs.

3

Add the grated cheese, 4 teaspoons of water, and mix.

4

Continue to add water, a little at a time, until the dough sticks together but is not soggy.

5

Roll out the pasty on a floured table-top until 1cm thick.

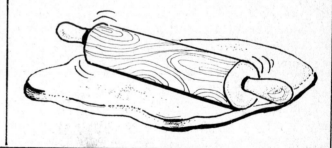

6

Cut into fingers, or any shape you like, and put them onto the greased baking tray to cook.

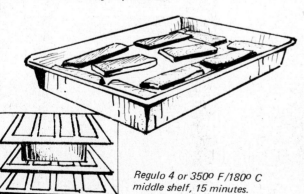

Regulo 4 or 350° F/180° C middle shelf, 15 minutes.

7

Allow your cheese straws to cool on a wire tray.

Greet the

In other words — try our fun quiz to find out what the New Year has in store for YOU, plus plenty of tips and information on pastimes, hobbies and ways of enjoying yourself, whatever the season, wherever you live, and whatever the weather!

2) What do you think of New Year resolutions?

a) It's fun to make a list of ridiculous resolutions, just for a giggle!

b) You only make those resolutions you mean to keep;

c) You nearly always make a list;

d) You hardly ever bother making any;

e) You never even think about it.

3) What about this ancient New Year's Day Charm to dream of the man you'll marry? Into a pint of cold spring water, beat a pullet's egg, (white, preferably) the legs of a spider and the ground-up skin of an eel, and drink before going to bed . . .
Suppose you were a girl in olden times, before the enlightened days of radio, television and mags like TAMMY — would you have believed it would work?

a) The thought of eating spider's legs would have put you off the idea, anyway!

b) You might have believed it — but you wouldn't have tried it.

c) Probably.

d) You might have tried it, if you didn't know the ingredients!

e) You'd have pretended to try it, then told everyone fantastic stories about the wonderful husband you'd dreamed about!

1) How would you most like to celebrate the New Year?

a) Ringing the New Year bells?

b) Enjoying yourself at a party?

c) Telephoning your love and best wishes to someone far away?

d) Trying out an ancient New Year charm, such as wishing on the Moon at midnight?

e) Singing "Auld Lang Syne" at home with your family?

4) Have you ever been, or welcomed, a "first-footer" into your home after midnight on the first day of a New Year — that "tall, dark stranger" who, by tradition, brings a piece of coal, a coin and some bread as symbols of prosperity to the family?

a) It sounds a spooky idea to open a door after midnight.

b) It's happened only once or twice in your family.

c) No — but you always hope it will happen!

d) No, but you'd like to 'first-foot" this New Year.

e) It's a custom you look forward to.

New Year!

5) What do you mostly look forward to on the first day of the New Year?

a) A few more days left of your school holidays?

b) Your summer holidays, with plenty of sunshine?

c) The thought that St. Valentine's Day isn't too far away?

d) Doing something really spectacular during the next twelve months?

e) Spring time, with Easter eggs and pretty flowers?

6) Have you ever kept a diary? (We mean ALL the year through, though not necessarily writing something every day!)

a) You never seem to have the time!

b) You've started a few times, but it usually peters out after a while?

c) Only for remembering dates and appointments?

d) Yes.

e) No — but you mean to start this year!

7) Which of these special days is likely to be most important to you?

a) St. Valentine's Day;

b) August Bank Holiday?

c) Hallowe'en;

d) Shrove Tuesday;

e) Guy Fawkes' Night.

8) Which date does your memory usually need a jog to remember?

a) Your best friend's birthday?

b) Father's Day?

c) Your Parents' Wedding Anniversary?

d) Mother's Day?

e) Dad's birthday?

9) Which "theme week" would appeal to you most in the coming year?

a) International Imagination Week?

b) "Let's-Be—Kind-To-Animals" Week?

c) "Song And Dance" Week?

d) "Nothing But Nonsense" Week?

e) "Exchange A Smile" Week?

10) Lastly, what would you most like to be able to say at the end of the year?

a) It brought many changes for the better.

b) That it was your happiest year so far.

c) You made some lasting friendships.

d) It was the year you finally achieved something special.

e) That the family came closer together.

TOT UP YOUR SCORE!

	a)	b)	c)	d)	e)
Question 1:	a) = 5;	b) = 4;	c) = 3;	d) = 2;	e) = 1;
Question 2:	a) = 4;	b) = 3;	c) = 2;	d) = 1;	e) = 5;
Question 3:	a) = 3;	b) = 2;	c) = 1;	d) = 5;	e) = 4;
Question 4:	a) = 2;	b) = 1;	c) = 5;	d) = 4;	e) = 3;
Question 5:	a) = 1;	b) = 5;	c) = 4;	d) = 3;	e) = 2;
Question 6:	a) = 5;	b) = 4;	c) = 3;	d) = 2;	e) = 1;
Question 7:	a) = 4;	b) = 3;	c) = 2;	d) = 1;	e) = 5;
Question 8:	a) = 3;	b) = 2;	c) = 1;	d) = 5;	e) = 4;
Question 9:	a) = 2;	b) = 1;	c) = 5;	d) = 4;	e) = 3;
Question 10:	a) = 1;	b) = 5;	c) = 4;	d) = 3;	e) = 2;

Grace's CASTLE

Brooke Castle had stood empty at the top of the hill for as long as Donna could remember. A long time ago, her gran said, there had been a family living there, with parties, servants and banquets. Now, there was nothing but half-ruined walls, rotting woodwork, and weeds growing high between the cracked paving stones.

But Donna didn't know much about the castle — until, staying with Gran during the winter school holiday, she heard her grand-dad commenting: "Another letter in the paper this week about the County Council turning Brooke Castle into some sort of Plea-sure Centre. Seems Bowman's — you know, the brewery family who own it — aren't keen on selling."

"Dreadful, the state it's in!" exclaimed Donna's gran. "Why, that castle goes back to the time of the first Lord Brooke, knighted by one of the King Henrys!"

Donna didn't say anything. But that was when she decided to take a closer look at the grey, crumbling building — for no better reason than to have something to do the next day.

She'd been expecting to find it a cold, lonely place with the wind whistling in through its gaping walls, making the thick, tall weeds rustle eerily.

Instead, the pale sun glowed quite cosily on the blotchy stone-work, even giving the rusty gates a dim sort of glow. Away from the wind, the castle felt quite warm, and with all the mossy patches on the stone floor, it was almost like walking on a carpet, Donna's footsteps hardly making a sound.

Suddenly, she wanted to call out: "Hello!" just to see if her voice would echo around the walls. But, it didn't.

Then she tried imagining what the castle might have been like with lots of velvet furni-ture, four-poster beds, and thick curtains. But that wasn't too easy, either.

"So, what's stopping that brewery family selling this to the County Council, like Grand-dad was saying?" Donna wondered aloud. "Could there be — buried treasure in hidden dungeons?" The silence seemed to tell her that it wasn't very likely.

"Maybe there's some legend about this place ..." Donna continued, beginning to enjoy herself. "Or ———" another thought crossed her mind, "or, ghosts! Ghosts of the family!" It seemed quite exciting to think of.

"Rubbish, child!" a voice rapped out at her, so unexpectedly that Donna whirled around in fright.

"I — I thought I was the only one here ..." she explained feebly, staring into brown eyes, glinting like an ever-watchful squirrel. Without the grey, bushy hair and wrinkled skin, they might have belonged to a girl like herself.

"Huh!" was all the old lady said, walking around Donna and tapping a knobbly-look-ing stick on the ground. "And I thought *I* was the only one here!"

Donna debated whether to smile, but decided against it.

"Er, I — I only came to explore a bit ..." she said, at last.

"Explore?"

"Yes ... You know — try and find out about the castle. My gran said a family once lived here, and they gave lots of big parties and everything ..."

"Quite right!" Donna was rather surprised to see the old lady nodding and smiling. "A fine place, this was!"

Donna's mouth opened wide. "You — you remember? Oh, couldn't you tell me some-thing about it?"

The old woman limped towards Donna, reaching out a skinny hand.

"I'll do more than that, girlie! Here, take my arm!"

"Now, all this," she went on, waving her stick, "was the main banqueting hall. Where we're standing would be the place where guests waited to have their names announced!"

"Ooooh!" Donna gasped, looking down. "To think, I'm standing where someone famous might've stood!"

"Yes, everyone came here, from miles around ... Now, all the beautiful pictures which hung from these walls, and the crystal

chandeliers . . . all gone . . ."

Slowly, the old woman turned her grey head and gazed out of an empty window frame. "My — my father always said he wanted his home to be a proper castle. And, he got his wish. We all loved it here . . ."

"Then, why ———?" began Donna, remembering what her granddad had said. But the old lady pressed a finger to her lips.

"Save your questions till I've shown you around. And you can tell me your name, and something about yourself."

"What shall I call you?"

"I think," said the old woman, "you might call me Grace."

Grace . . . It was a good name for her, Donna thought, watching her going up the stone steps which had once led to the music room; or walking along the ruined Minstrels' Gallery; eagerly pointing out the remains of a Tudor fireplace; or the niches in the walls of the kitchen gardens where beehives were kept, in the days when everything had to be sweetened with honey, instead of sugar.

"Well!" breathed Donna, as they neared the banqueting hall once more. "I said I wanted to find out something about Brooke Castle! But — I still don't understand . . ." she bit her lip.

"Tell me what you were going to say," Grace urged gently. "Something to do with selling Brooke Castle?"

"Well, why *don't* you sell it to the County Council, like they want?" Donna blurted out. "It isn't as if you can keep it going, and — and ———"

"And they want to make it into some sort of tourist attraction!" Grace spat out the words in disgust. "Somewhere for people who care so much about the castle, that they've never bothered about it before, not even to do some weeding, or even brushing the steps now and again! So, what do they *really* care?"

She looked angry, yet so weak and feeble that Donna wanted to cry.

"I understand how you feel, Grace, really I do. But, if you sold out ———"

"If I sold out, it would be my home gone for ever! I could never come here again, to remember Brooke Castle as it used to be. And it's still home — home for the creatures that are happy to stay here. No! The castle's better left as it is!"

Donna looked so upset by this outburst that Grace squeezed her hand.

"Now, don't you fret about an old woman's fancies, Donna. You come and see me again, and I'll show you where the squirrels and rabbits play, and where the badgers will have their babies in the spring!"

Donna smiled gratefully. "That'd be lovely, Grace! See you tomorrow, then?"

"Very well. Now, off you go . . . Oh, and if you see my chauffeur standing by the car at the foot of the hill, no need to say anything. He knows I'll be coming along shortly."

Donna couldn't help being impressed. "All right, Grace! 'Bye!" And she began skipping down the hill, looking back at the thin, frail figure which waved to her.

"Talk about making friends in high places!" she murmured, as she saw the gleaming Rolls-Royce car, standing just where Grace said it would be. The driver, sitting at the wheel reading his newspaper, didn't notice Donna, although she did turn to give him a smile, just in case he happened to look up.

She couldn't wait to tell her gran all about meeting Grace.

"The way she showed me around Brooke Castle!" she babbled excitedly. "It was just like being an important person!"

"And — her name was Grace?" Gran inquired thoughtfully.

"Yes!"

"There was a daughter in the Bowman family, name of Grace," Granddad put in, tapping his pipe against the fireplace. "I thought she died, though."

"I was thinking the same, soon as Donna mentioned her name," agreed Gran. "But then, we've probably got things a bit mixed up!"

"Probably . . ." Granddad still looked thoughtful. "After all, it were a big family."

"Anyway," Donna interrupted, "she's got a car with her own driver. And she knows every inch of that castle. I'm seeing her again, tomorrow!"

And, she did — this time where the greenhouses had once been, and where a stray cat was now suckling a family of four kittens.

"I've lost count of the number of mother-cats who've come here," Grace said, emptying some scraps onto a sheet of newspaper. Even in the old days, it was the same."

"Granddad was telling me about your family," Donna informed her. "Not that he remembered much — except that there were quite a few children."

"That was a long time ago," Grace smiled gently. "Now, shall we see if the squirrels are anywhere around the ballroom? The weather's mild enough!"

Donna's granddad grew more and more interested about Grace.

"My friend's dad used to get the tennis court ready for Master Henry at Brooke Castle," he explained. "Wonder what became of him?"

"I'll ask Grace, shall I?" Donna suggested eagerly. "Mind you, she doesn't talk much about her family . . ."

The tennis court, Donna discovered, was still there, even though the grass had covered the white lines.

"Yes, Henry was a fine player," Grace confirmed. "But," and Donna was dismayed to see her turning away clumsily, "I-I'd rather not talk about it."

Soon, Grace was chatting to Donna, about the deer which famous nobles used to hunt in Elizabethan times in the grounds of Brooke Castle. But, that didn't stop Donna thinking . . . What had happened to make her so upset when she mentioned her brother, Henry . . .?

"Maybe it's because Henry's dead, now," Donna's granddad guessed. "It takes a long time for people to forget, Donna."

"Yes, I know . . ." Donna wished she could explain. "But . . . you'd think someone else would want to visit the castle sometimes, and see Grace — offer to help her. The only other person I ever see is the man who drives that big car of hers . . ."

"All sorts of people get lonely, love." Granddad patted her shoulder, his shaggy eyebrows crinkling as he smiled. "Maybe that's why she's taken a fancy to you, having someone she can share her memories with. I'd say that was the reason she don't want to sell up."

Granddad could be right, Donna thought afterwards, listening to Gran arguing about the cost of getting the castle safe, and whether or not anyone could really afford to run it.

"I just don't know what to think," Donna confessed, the next time she managed to raise the subject. "You see, Grace — I mean, what happens when you . . . I mean, when ———"

"When I die?" Grace smiled gently. "Child, the castle is coming to the end of its days, just as I am. That's why I love it so, because it makes me feel that I'm not alone, because we are part of each other. I suppose that sounds silly ———!"

Her hoarse chuckle quickly turned into a series of hacking coughs which made her tired eyes water and her thin shoulders shake violently.

"Grace, you must come and sit down!" Donna insisted. "Or shall I fetch your driver?"

"No!" Grace barked out with a flash of strength. "I-I'll be all right in a moment. It-it's only this heavy wind that seems to have sprung up from nowhere . . ."

But she allowed Donna to lead her to the steps which had once wound down to the wine cellars, her frail old back leaning against part of the iron gate.

"I-I've always loved this place, Donna . . ." she jerked out painfully. "Always . . . I-I don't want it to change, not ever . . ." She shivered, and Donna took her hand.

"Grace, come home with me! Gran and Granddad would love to meet you, I know . . ."

"You're a kind girl, Donna." Grace's voice trembled. "B-but I have to be going, soon. Isn't that the church clock striking three?"

Donna listened. "Yes, I-I think so . . . But, Grace ———"

"You must leave, child. Just let me stay here a moment, at my castle . . ."

Donna hoped she wouldn't cry, not until she had waved to Grace as usual, and run down the hill. Was it because Grace was looking so ill? Or, so alone? She didn't know . . . And she didn't know whether to feel uneasy or relieved at seeing no sign of the big black car. At least, now, she needn't worry about breaking her promise and telling the driver how ill Grace had been . . . But the thought gave her little comfort as she walked back, her head bent against the fierce wind, which made her feel as if she had a great, heavy burden on her shoulders.

Gran and Granddad were busy talking in the living room as she came in.

"I knew I was right about the Bowman family dying out," Granddad was saying. "It was because the castle was in a Trust Fund that made things difficult for the County Council!"

"Yet, the library says there was a daughter, called Grace . . ." came Gran's sensible voice. "And from what Donna's told us — well, who else could she be? Even if she were supposed to be dead these past ten years . . ."

Dead. The word seemed to whirl around Donna's mind. Dead . . . Dead . . . Her footsteps thudded on the ground as she began running, the wind howling behind her.

"Grace!" she screamed out, as soon as the castle came into sight. "Grace!" But the wind snatched away her words, others piercing her aching head.

"Dead these past ten years . . ."

"Maybe there's some tragic legend . . . Or, ghosts of the family . . ."

"Grace!" she yelled again, at the same time wondering why she was calling her name, especially against the noise of the wind and the trees rustling loudly all around her.

There was another sound, now — a sound which felt like a deep rumble of thunder from below the ground, which spread outwards, growing steadily louder, until it exploded in a great burst of noise, sending thick showers of dust and bits of brick and stone which, even in the dim light, Donna could see leaping into the air, as the crumbling old stonework tumbled to the ground, where once a tennis court and a Deer Park had been.

"Grace!" Donna screamed again, scrambling frantically towards the castle. "Grace!"

"Easy, young lady, easy!" someone shouted above the roar. "This was bound to happen some day, and in a gale-force wind like this, the old place had no chance!"

"B-but, you don't understand!" Donna heard herself shouting desperately. "Grace — she-she's in there! I know she is!"

"No," comforted a fireman, grasping Donna's arm. "The place was absolutely deserted — not even a mouse in sight. We made sure of that, soon as the Mayor's chauffeur sounded the alarm when he saw signs that the main hall was crumbling!"

Donna blinked fiercely, as if to make quite sure that the kindly face looking at her was the same one she'd seen so often, bent over a paper in the driving seat of a very large, black car . . .

"Y-you're the Mayor's chauffeur?" she said at last. "You were always waiting at the bottom of the hill . . ."

"Yes, waiting for the Mayor, so that I could drive him to Council meetings."

Dead. The word flashed again into Donna's mind.

Ghosts of the family.

It seemed a while before she realised that the driver was still talking to her.

"Aren't you the girl I've noticed waving to old Nelly? Is that why you're here now?"

"Not *Nelly*!" Donna could have wept with impatience. "Grace! She showed me around the castle, telling me what it was like when she lived there . . ." Her words faltered to a stop. Gran said Grace died over ten years ago . . .

"I-I'm very sorry ———" Donna could see the man was wondering what to say. "I didn't know . . . She didn't talk to many people . . ."

"What are you talking about?" Donna shouted at him. "What are you trying to say?"

The man took a deep breath. "Your friend wasn't Grace Bowman. It was Nelly White, whose father was an under-gardener. That's why she knew everything about the place."

"I-I don't believe it!" Donna didn't bother to brush away the tears which sprang to her eyes. "She — she wouldn't lie to me!"

"Not lies — at least, not to Nelly. More of an old woman's dream of things that might have been. Brooke Castle was all she ever talked about at the Old People's Home where she lived — you should've heard her telling the Mayor about it when he visited there last year! That's why she always loved coming back here, to the only proper home she'd ever known."

Donna turned her tear-filled eyes towards the mounds of crumbling bricks, still sending up sprays of dust and rubble high into the air.

"The castle is coming to the end of its days. It makes me feel that I am not alone, because we are part of each other . . ." Grace had said. Had said. And the man said: "She always loved coming here." Loved.

Donna's throat suddenly felt very tight.

"Grace!" she cried out, grabbing the man's arm. "What's happened to her?"

Even before he spoke, she knew the answer.

"Nelly? She'd been ill for some time, you know. Matron wanted to keep her in bed today, seeing how weak she was. But Nelly said she had to meet somebody — and that was you, wasn't it?" Donna nodded miserably.

"When she didn't come back by three o'clock, Matron guessed something must have happened. And remembering her love for Brooke Castle, she and the doctor came straight here . . . It seemed she'd had a heart attack, just there." And he pointed to the wine cellar steps, where Donna had seen Grace — she would never be able to think of her as Nelly — giving her a last, feeble wave of her hand.

"It's three o'clock . . ." she remembered her last words again. "You must leave . . ."

But, had she heard the clock striking, Donna wondered? Or — had her friend come back to meet her, as she promised? Perhaps she would never really know . . .

"Sorry, lass," the driver was saying. "The place won't make any Pleasure Centre now, will it? Only fit for birds, and animals and that . . ."

"Yes . . ." Donna remembered the kittens, the squirrels and the birds which had been so dear to Grace. "Yes — it's their home, now."

"And that's what you'd have wanted, isn't it, Grace?" Donna was speaking to herself — yet she knew that somebody, somewhere would hear, through the wind and the rain.

It made her believe there might still be something to be happy about, after all.

Wee Sue

Little Sue Strong had just returned from a few days holiday and was glad to meet up with a bunch of her friends...

EVERYONE WELCOME! COME TO THE NEW MILLTOWN SPORTS CENTRE - PLEASE!

COR! THAT NEW INDOOR SPORTS CENTRE'S OPENED WHILE I'VE BEEN AWAY! COMING TO GIVE IT A ONCE-OVER, MATES?

NO FEAR! EVERYONE SAYS IT'S A DEAD LOSS!

THEY SAY IT'S ONLY FOR YOUR DEAD KEEN ATHLETES! NOT FOR THE LIKES OF US WHO JUST WANT A BIT OF FUN!

YEAH. WE LIKED THE OLD SPORTS HALL, BUT THEY CLOSED IT DOWN. YOU COMIN' TO THE COFFEE BAR, SUE?

NO, THINK I'LL CHECK THE PLACE OUT FOR MYSELF.

HELLO, LOOKS LIKE MY MATES WERE WRONG! THE NEW SPORTS CENTRE **MUST** BE POPULAR! LOOK AT THAT CROWD — AND THAT'S JUST OUTSIDE!

IT PAYS TO BE SHORT IF YOU WANT TO GET THROUGH A CROWD IN A HURRY! HEY, THE PLACE IS PRETTY WELL DESERTED INSIDE!

Then, an unwelcome familiar voice hailed Sue...

SUE—SUE STRONG! COME HERE... I WANT YOUR HELP!

CRIKEY. IT'S MISS BIGGER! WHAT ON EARTH'S SHE DOING HERE?

THE—ER—REGULAR NETBALL REFEREE RESIGNED YESTERDAY, AND I'VE BEEN ROPED IN TO HANDLE THIS EXTREMELY IMPORTANT MATCH. WE'RE ONE PLAYER SHORT, THOUGH, SO...

I KNOW — YOU'RE ROPING ME IN TO MAKE UP THE TEAM? OKAY, MISS BIGGER!

Meanwhile, unbeknown to Sue, the real reason for the crowd's presence was revealed outside...

BTV OUTSIDE BROADCAST.

OOH, IT'S MICHAEL CARROT FROM 'COUNTRYWIDE'!

AND SO FROM THE HISTORIC HIGH STREET OF MILLTOWN... WE COME TO WHAT HAS BEEN DESCRIBED AS THE COUNCIL'S BIGGEST BLUNDER EVER... THE NEW INDOOR SPORTS CENTRE! IT SEEMS NO ONE WANTS TO USE IT...

WHY? BECAUSE THEY SAY IT'S INTENDED JUST FOR SUPER ATHLETES, NOT THE MAN, OR — ER — WOMAN ON THE STREET. LET'S LOOK INSIDE...

Inside, the netball match was underway — much to Sue's discomfort...

PUFF! TEN MINUTES SOLID RUNNING...

...AND IN ALL THAT TIME, PANT!...

Perhaps not so lucky . . .

I COULD DO WITH A HAND TO GET OUTTA HERE, OOW — LEGGO — I DIDN'T MEAN THAT!

YAKIRI, AH SO!

TRUST ME TO RUN INTO A JUDO EXPERT. LUCKY THIS TRAMPOLINE WAS HERE!

I SAY THERE . . . YOU LOOK A JOLLY GROUP! WOULD YOU CARE TO SAY A FEW WORDS TO OUR TELEVISION VIEWERS?

GOTCHER! NOW, TO . . .

CLONK!

The magic word — television!

. . . WELL, AS YOU CAN SEE . . . IT'S SMILES ALL ROUND AT THE MILLTOWN SPORTS CENTRE, THOUGH NO ONE SEEMS TOO KEEN TO MAKE ANY COMMENTS! SO, WITH THAT, IT'S BACK TO OUR LONDON STUDIO!

MY CUE TO SLIP OUT!

The 'countrywide' feature on Milltown Sports Centre was screened the next day . . .

MILLTOWN INDOOR SPORTS CENTRE — A MECCA OF SPORTING FUN FOR ALL, OR BORING, "ATHLETES-ONLY" FAILURE? OUR HIDDEN CAMERS INSTALLED THERE YESTERDAY REVEAL THE ANSWER!

HUH! NO ONE TOLD ME THERE WERE TV CAMERAS THERE! I'VE MADE A RIGHT MUCK UP OF THINGS!

HEE, HEE! AS YOU SEE, NETBALL IS ONE OF THE CENTRE'S BIGGEST 'DRAWERS'. CHUCKLE!

OH, NO ! 'THE LYNCH MOB'LL BE AFTER ME, NOW!

WELL, HA, HA! THEY CERTAINLY DON'T TAKE THEIR TENNIS TOO SERIOUSLY AT MILLTOWN . . . CHUCKLE . . . THE NET RESULT BEING A GOOD LAUGH ALL ROUND! HO, HO!

. . . AND WHAT BETTER WAY TO END A DAY'S LIGHT-HEARTED SPORT THAN BY A HECTIC GAME OF, ER, TAG! HO, HO!

YES, AND A GOOD TIME WAS HAD BY ALL! SO MUCH SO THAT IN THE LAST FIVE MINUTES OUR SWITCH-BOARD'S BEEN JAMMED WITH CALLERS ASKING HOW TO GET TO THIS GREAT CENTRE OF ENTERTAINMENT! MILLTOWN INDOOR SPORTS CENTRE, 'COUNTRYWIDE' HAVE VOTED YOU "FUN-PLACE OF THE WEEK!"

And, at the Milltown Sports Centre next day . . .

WELL, THINGS HAVE CHANGED! THE CENTRE'S PACKED SOLID! NOT EVEN ROOM FOR A LITTLE'UN LIKE ME. WHICH IS JUST AS WELL, 'COS . . .

. . . THAT MEANS I'VE A SPORTING CHANCE OF GETTING THROUGH THIS LITTLE LOT BEFORE TEA-TIME! HO, HO!

EAT UP, SUE . . . ALL IS FORGIVEN!

A TOAST TO WEE SUE! THE LITTLE LADY WHO PUT US IN THE BIG TIME!

BESSIE BUNTER

IT'S A PUZZLE

* *

1. **JOLLY JIGSAW**
Only one of these pieces fits properly to complete the jigsaw. Which one is it?

ANSWER:

Piece D.

2. **REAL SHADY**
Shade in the areas marked with a cross in brown and those marked with a dot in yellow, to find something that was used many years ago, but is still seen now on special occasions.

ANSWER:

A gun-carriage.

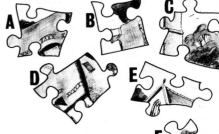

3. **DRIVE YOU DOTTY**
See what picture you get by joining all the dots from 1 to 118.

ANSWER:

A showjumper.

30

4. CUSHION COVERS

These cushions are made of different fabrics. Re-arrange the letters to find what the materials are.

ANSWER:
Satin, hessian, velvet, tweed, crash, brocade.

RUSTY
SELF
SOLD
ROCKET
COALS
QUOTAS
CROCHET

5. SPORTING SWITCH

Replace two letters in each word with two other letters, so that they spell the name of a game.

ANSWER:
Rugby, golf, polo, hockey, bowls, quoits, croquet.

CABUSEE TEYH TOHB VEAH KSURTN

6. QUICK RIDDLE

See how quickly you can read this riddle. The answer to it is in the jumbled words below.

ANSWER:
Why is an elephant like a tree? Because they both have trunks!

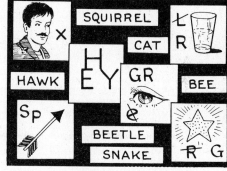

7. ANIMAL PUZZLE

The names of six creatures are hidden here. Solve the picture clues, then add the correct word to follow and so complete the name.

ANSWER:
Manx-cat, grass snake, honey-bee, grey squirrel, sparrow-hawk, stag-beetle.

8. PICTURE FIT

Solve the picture clues, then see if you can fit the words into the blank spaces to make a different word.

ANSWER:
Chilly, granted, swallow, weighty, street, scarlet.

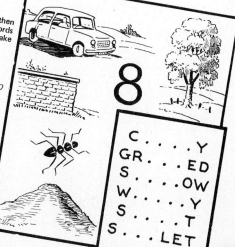

C . . . . . Y
GR . . . ED
S . . . . OW
W . . . . . Y
S . . . . T
S . . . LET

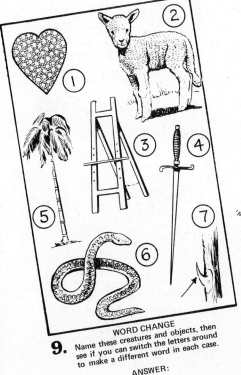

9. WORD CHANGE

Name these creatures and objects, then see if you can switch the letters around to make a different word in each case.

ANSWER:
1. *Heart — earth.* 2. *Lamb — balm.*
3. *Easel — lease.* 4. *Sword — words.*
5. *Palm — lamp.* 6. *Snake — sneak.*
7. *Thorn — north.*

Bella

After a hard struggle to make her way as a gymnast, Bella Barlow had become a member of the flourishing Collington Club where her talent was quickly recognised. Just now, tests were being held to select a team for the Anglia All-Comers' Championships . . .

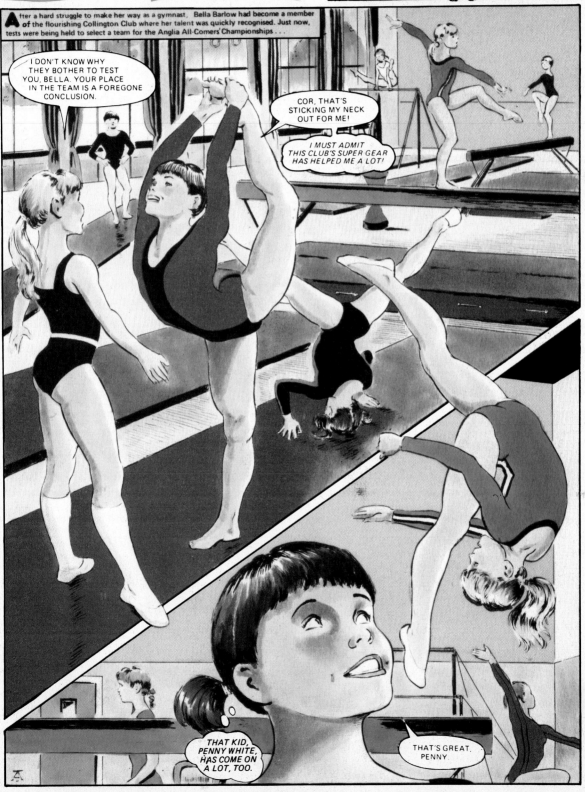

I DON'T KNOW WHY THEY BOTHER TO TEST YOU, BELLA. YOUR PLACE IN THE TEAM IS A FOREGONE CONCLUSION.

COR, THAT'S STICKING MY NECK OUT FOR ME!

I MUST ADMIT THIS CLUB'S SUPER GEAR HAS HELPED ME A LOT!

THAT KID, PENNY WHITE, HAS COME ON A LOT, TOO.

THAT'S GREAT, PENNY.

35

BUT BELLA, THEY'VE NOT INCLUDED YOU.

YOU'RE RIGHT, THEY HAVEN'T.

WELL, YOU DID MAKE RATHER A LOT OF BOOBS.

THERE MUST BE A MISTAKE.

THERE'S NO MISTAKE, BELLA. THEY COULDN'T POSSIBLY HAVE PICKED YOU AFTER THAT TEST. AFTER ALL MY COACHING! WHAT EVER GOT INTO YOU?

I — I DON'T KNOW, EXACTLY.

I'VE LET DOWN THE COACH AND SPOILT MY CHANCES. I COULDN'T EXPLAIN IT BEGAN BY WANTING TO HELP PENNY.

THE ANGLIA MEETING IS A QUALIFIER FOR THE INTERNATIONAL —

AARGH!

YOU STUPID LITTLE JAY-WALKER! LOOK WHAT YOU'VE MADE ME DO TO MY CAR!

OH, GOSH! OH, I'M TERRIBLY SORRY.

I DEPEND ON HER FOR MY JOB, AND I'M ONLY INSURED THIRD-PARTY. YOU DON'T LOOK LIKELY TO FOOT THE BILL.

OF COURSE I'LL PAY. ONLY GIVE ME A LITTLE TIME. . .

37

AND THE HORSE IS LAME IN ONE LEG!

A GOOD GRIP CHANGE, KATE.

SHE'D FIND IT EASIER IF THOSE OLD BARS HADN'T LOST MOST OF THEIR "GIVE". GOSH, I REALISE NOW HOW TIP-TOP THE COLLINGTON STUFF IS — CHAMOIS-COVERED BEAMS, FOAM PIT, SPRUNG FLOOR, THE LOT!

Some time later . . .

THAT'S THE CAR DAMAGE PAID OFF. I'VE FINISHED AT HANDY ANDY'S CAFÉ, WHICH GIVES ME JUST A WEEK OF REGULAR TRAINING BEFORE THE CHAMPIONSHIPS.

PENSIONS

The week went in a flash. Then. . .

NOW GIRLS, KEEP TOGETHER WHILE I FIND OUT WHERE WE GO.

WE'RE BARMY COMING. WE'LL HAVE THE LOWEST SCORE OF ALL!

Inside . . .

OH, GOSH! IT'S ALL MUCH GRANDER THAN I EXPECTED!

AND EVERYONE ELSE HAS GOT SUCH FANTASTIC KIT, WHEREAS OURS . . .

IT'S NOT A FASHION SHOW! IT'S WHAT YOU DO THAT COUNTS.

OH, BELLA, I'M SO GLAD YOU'VE MADE IT.

NOT MUCH TROUBLE GETTING INTO THAT TEAM. NO WONDER IT'S CALLED VICTORIA. THAT OLD DAME CAN'T BE THE COACH, SURELY?

I SAID ALL ALONG WE WERE BARMY TO COME.

I SUPPOSE WE COULD STILL WITHDRAW, BELLA?

THEN WE WOULD LOOK PROPER CHARLIES! COME ON, TIME TO WARM UP.

MAKING THEM ENTER WAS MY ONLY WAY OF GETTING HERE. BUT IS IT TOO CRUEL, LETTING THEM IN FOR SUCH AN ORDEAL?

The competition began. . .

NEVER SEEN KATE WORK SO WELL ON THE BEAM BEFORE.

Bella's turn came . . .

EEK! SUDDENLY SEEMS EASY!

BOTH YOU AND NORAH HAVE DONE BETTER VAULTS THAN EVER!

WE'VE NEVER HAD SUCH GOOD APPARATUS BEFORE!

THAT'S THE ANSWER! AFTER TRAINING ON THEIR OLD GEAR, THIS SEEMS CHILD'S PLAY.

The Victoria girls went from strength to strength. . .

I KNEW KATE HAD ABILITY, BUT THIS SPRUNG FLOOR IS GIVING AN EDGE TO HER ROUTINE.

ALL THROUGH THE YEAR

YOU can make pretty things for yourself, your family and your friends, throughout the year, by using bits and pieces which you can lay hands on without too much bother, and some Gloy Children's Glue.

This is specially good for young people to use, because it washes easily off hands, clothes and furniture if you happen to have any mishaps.

Calendar

So, why not start at the very beginning of the year by making a calendar? All you need is some plain cardboard — the back section of a shoe-box is ideal — or the main piece of a greetings card presentation box. (There are usually plenty of those around after Christmas!)

Trim any whiskery edges off your card, then choose some bits and pieces to make a nice design. You can see the effect of flowers and dried leaves in the photograph. How about that gorgeous butterfly made from just five evergreen leaves and a piece of dried stem? You may like to use sweet wrappings from a Christmas pack, ribbon-trims from your favourite present, or bits cut from Christmas cards . . . you're bound to come across lots of things which would look nice!

Arrange your design as you want it, then draw around each piece with a pencil, so that you know where everything is meant to go. Take each piece in your design, and carefully apply the glue, gently pressing down each section of the design with a piece of clean blotting paper.

When you've finished, cover with a piece of Gloy Coverfilm, cut just a little larger than the size of your design. Coverfilm is a transparent sticky-back plastic which you can buy in a roll from art shops and stationers in a choice of four tints, as well as the clear. It will give your design a lovely shiny, wipe-clean finish "for keeps"!

Make two holes, either with a paper-punch or knitting needle, at the top of your design to thread a scrap of ribbon or wool through, knotting firmly on the "wrong" side.

Then cut two lengths of ribbon about 1½" (4 cm), and apply glue to the bottom ½" (1 cm) of each ribbon piece, attaching this to the back of a calendar-book. Then, apply the glue to the top ½" (1 cm) and stick to the back of your design, so that the calendar hangs below, as in the photograph — and your calendar's all ready to hand over as a present to last the whole year through!

Easter chick

Next comes Easter — and what better way to celebrate than with a string of paper chicks to decorate an Easter present or breakfast table; or you could make a whole line to hang up in your class room or march along the window sill! All you need are some strips of paper 30 cm (12") x 3 cm (1¼"). Sugar paper is best, and you can generally buy this by the sheet and in a choice of colours from stationers and art shops. Or, you could try using strips of fairly thick writing paper coloured with felt-tipped pens or crayons.

Once you've cut your strip, make a "Figure 8" shape (see our sketch), with one large loop and one small loop, sticking the ends into place with the Children's Glue, to make the body and head of your Easter chick.

To make the "comb", cut a small oblong of paper and fold it into three equal sections lengthways. Open out and bring the lengthways edges together, so that you can cut the wavy shape of the top of the comb. Now, lay the middle section of the comb piece

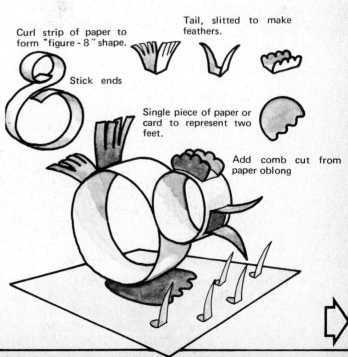

Curl strip of paper to form "figure - 8" shape.

Stick ends

Tail, slitted to make feathers.

Single piece of paper or card to represent two feet.

Add comb cut from paper oblong

model on the right, complete with little pebbles stuck inside the shell with the Children's Glue. But you could just colour the inside centre of the shell with a black felt-tipped pen, if you preferred.

Black mussel shells have been used for the feet, and a winkle shell for the "nose" of the larger model, with a fragment from a large shell for the flat hat. You might also like to choose a nice, flat pebble from the beach or garden on which to mount your shell man.

Just a few tips to remember. When you are joining two hinged scallop shells, it helps to rub the edges to be stuck together with a scrap of medium sandpaper, so that the surfaces will bond more easily. A blob or two of Plasticene is also useful to hold shells in position while you apply the glue, and allow it to dry.

You'll find shells are very good-tempered when it comes to painting. You can either use felt-tipped pens, modelling enamel, or dregs of household paint or nail varnish. For quickness, drop some shells into the bottom of an almost-empty paint tin, give it a good shake, and see what lovely colours you get when you tip them out on a piece of plain paper to dry!

Crackers

To help fill a few long winter evenings, why not have a go at making your own Christmas Crackers? As well as being a favourite table decoration and party novelty, some special Christmas crackers made with Gloy Children's Glue make gorgeous gift-wraps — and just think of the useful things you could put inside . . . packets of needles, shampoos combs or shoe-laces.

at the top of the chick's head, as in our drawing, so that you can see how it will look, and cut to size if necessary before applying glue to the underside of the middle section and sticking into place.

The tail is just a larger oblong piece of paper folded in half and cut tail-shaped; with four or five slits cut into it to make the "feathers". Flatten out the fold to make a wider centre section, so that you can apply glue and stick it into place. Make the beak piece in much the same way, as you can see in the photograph.

Cut two feet from one piece of paper (you could use card for this), to help the chick stand up. Remember to leave a straight strip at the top for you to stick to the base of the chick's body.

Shell time

Summer time is usually "shell time" for many of us. But how many times have you collected shells, then put them in a drawer, and forgotten about them? Well, this year, there's no excuse not to make a pretty and maybe unusual souvenir to remind you of your holiday!

Apart from Gloy Children's Glue to stick the shells into place, you need only one other thing — and that's imagination. The scallop shells you can see pictured above are very common and come in almost all colours and sizes. "Hinged", they make good head and body shapes — either widthways, as with the figure on the left, or lengthways, as you can see on the right.

"Single" scallop shells (un-hinged) have been used both for the "closed" eyes of the little man on the left, and the "arms" and open eyes of the other

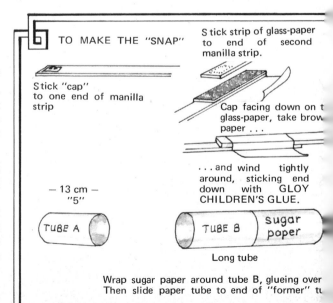

TO MAKE THE "SNAP"

Stick "cap" to one end of manilla strip

Stick strip of glass-paper to end of second manilla strip.

Cap facing down on t glass-paper, take brow paper . . .

. . . and wind tightly around, sticking end down with GLOY CHILDREN'S GLUE.

— 13 cm —
"5"

TUBE A

TUBE B

sugar poper

Long tube

Wrap sugar paper around tube B, glueing over
Then slide paper tube to end of "former" tu

YEAR

Her's what you will need for each one:

1 "outer" of coloured crêpe paper, 25.5 cm x 20.5 cm (10" x 8"); 1 "inner" of kitchen paper, 23.5 cm x 19 cm (9¼" x 7½"); 1 piece of sugar paper, 16 cm x 13 cm (6¼" x 5"); The item you want to put inside the cracker, and 1 home-made "snap".

Here's how to make that: Cut two thin strips of manilla paper, 16 cm x 7 mm (6¼" x 2¾"). and one strip of sand-paper 3 cm x 7mm (1¼" x 2¾"). In case you don't know, sand-paper (or glass-paper) is the stuff Dad might use to smooth down wood or paintwork. You can buy a sheet very cheaply from your nearest hardware shop.

Also, cut one percussion cap from a roll which you can buy for about 10p in any toy shop, and one piece of brown paper 3 cm x 3 cm (1¼" x 1¼").

Use glue to stick the sand-paper to the end of one manilla strip, and a cap to the other strip. Then, stick one end of the small piece of brown paper to the underside of the strip with the glass-paper on it, as in our sketch. Place the two strips together, with the cap facing the glass-paper, and wrap tightly with the brown paper, sticking down the end. When the cracker is pulled, and the strips part, the sand-paper will rub against the cap and make it "snap".

To make the actual cracker, cut two tubes from a packing roll — for example the type in which posters are mailed. Your local stationer or newsagent may let you have one for nothing, if you ask.

The tubes should measure 22 cm long x 4 cm diameter (8¾" x 1½") and II cm x 4 cm, (4½" x 1½"). These will be used as "formers" to get the shape of your cracker.

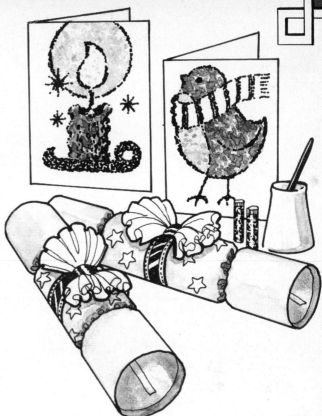

Roll the piece of sugar paper around the longer tube, and glue the overlapping edge. Then you can slide the sugar paper tube to the end of the "former" (see our sketch).

Place the crêpe paper on a flat working surface and arrange the formers (A — short, B — long), as shown in the sketch. Place the "snap" into position, then roll the pieces together and stick down the open end.

Carefully pull out tube "A" for about 2.5cm (1"), then use a piece of strong thread to tie the cracker end, so that you can put a paper hat, joke or motto, present — whatever you like — inside.

Hold the cracker in the middle to prevent the sugar paper roll from coming out, and carefully take out the long tube until there is a gap of 2.5 cm (1") between the end of the tube and the sugar paper roll inside. Tie this end of the cracker (as you can see in our sketch), and complete by decorating with pom-poms, motifs, sections cut from Christmas cards, and use Gloy Glitter, fixed with some glue, for that special Christmas sparkle!

Christmas cards

And Gloy Glitter is the secret of those sparkly cards, shown above, too. Just write your message and draw your design, go over it with glue, then sprinkle on the glitter, as thick as you like. Shake the excess onto a sheet of paper, and it's all ready to use again for some more Christmas greetings!

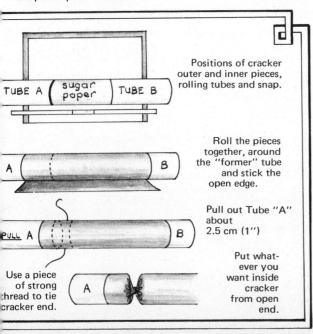

Positions of cracker outer and inner pieces, rolling tubes and snap.

TUBE A | sugar paper | TUBE B

Roll the pieces together, around the "former" tube and stick the open edge.

A _____ B

Pull out Tube "A" about 2.5 cm (1")

PULL A _____ B

Put whatever you want inside cracker from open end.

Use a piece of strong thread to tie cracker end.

A

THE SPACE GIRL

"THERE ARE MORE THINGS IN HEAVEN AND EARTH,.," WROTE SHAKESPEARE. KELLY GOSNELL CERTAINLY BELIEVED THAT, FOR SHE WAS MAD KEEN ON SCIENCE FICTION...

WHERE'S OUR DAUGHTER — OUT PLAYING AT BEING A SPACE EXPLORER AGAIN?

I EXPECT SO, DEAR. I WISH KELLY WOULD TAKE AN INTEREST IN MORE LADYLIKE THINGS.

SHE SHOULD HAVE GROWN OUT OF BEING A TOMBOY AT HER AGE.

THERE'S FAR TOO MUCH NONSENSE ABOUT CREATURES FROM OTHER PLANETS ON TELEVISION THESE DAYS — THAT'S THE TROUBLE.

ANYWAY, I'M GOING TO HAVE A BATH BEFORE DINNER.

WHAT THE DEUCE — ?

VAL — WHAT ARE OUR PET FISH DOING IN THE BATH?

HI, MUM — DAD!

KELLY, WITH THE FISH BOWL AND MY NEW METALLIC RAINCOAT!

WE WERE EXPLORING A NEW PLANET. I LOOKED A REAL SPACE-WOMAN IN THAT AND THE COAT, BUT JIM AND BOB HAD TO PRETEND TO BE SCALEY MONSTERS WITH EIGHT SLIMY TENTACLES!

IF THERE ARE OTHER CREATURES IN THE UNIVERSE, WHAT MAKES YOU THINK THEY'RE MONSTERS?

OUR TEACHER SAID SO!

SHE SAID IT'S UN- LIKELY ANY OTHER LIFE-FORMS WOULD HAVE DEVELOPED THE SAME WAY WE HAVE. SHE SAID THAT TO US THEY'D PROBABLY APPEAR HORRIBLE!

OH SHE DID DID SHE? I'M GOING TO HAVE A WORD WITH HER RIGHT NOW!

THESE ARE TERRIFIC, DAD! AND IN THIS GEAR I FEEL LIKE IT'S REALLY HAPPENING!

ER, I THINK I'LL MAKE US A DRINK.

WAIT, I-I'LL HELP YOU! BIT MUCH FOR ME, TOO, ALL THIS!

A little later...

AW, ALL THOSE FILMS ARE SO SAMEY. I THINK I'LL GO UP IN MY TREE HOUSE AND READ A GOOD BOOK INSTEAD.

HEY, IT WORKED!

I'VE GOT THIS SMASHING BOOK JERRY LENT ME!

OH NO! BACK TO SQUARE ONE.

4000 AD

But just then...

SIGH! CAN'T YOU GET IT INTO YOUR HEAD THERE ARE NO SUCH THINGS AS CREATURES ON OTHER PLANETS? WHAT'S IN THE PAPER, THEN?

GOSH! YOU'RE NOT GOING TO LIKE THIS ONE LITTLE BIT, DAD!

I BET THEY'VE GOT THREE HEADS AND ARE TWENTY FOOT TALL!

EVENING ECHO
XYNON EDITION
LATE NEWS

SPACE PROBE REVEALS TRACES OF LIFE-FORMS ON PLANET EARTH!

The annual school outing had come round again and this time it was a trip to the seaside. . .

COME ALONG, GIRLS. WE'LL LOOK AROUND THE SHOPS FOR A WHILE THEN SUNBATHE ON THE BEACH.

COR, LUCKY, AIN'T THEY! IF ONLY WE WERE IN MISS BREWSTER'S GROUP.

OUR DAY WILL NOT BE SO WASTEFUL. WE'LL TOUR THE HISTORICAL BUILDINGS IN THE TOWN.

AND TO THINK I HAD ME BIKINI PRESSED SPECIALLY!

PHEW, IT'S HOT — CAN'T WE GET SOME ICE CREAMS, MISS?

CERTAINLY NOT — DISGUSTING HABIT! NOW, DO COME ALONG. NO DAWDLING, BEST FOOT FORWARD.

I WISH SHE'D MISSED THE COACH — ME FEET ARE KILLIN' ME.

IMAGINE YOURSELVES ON THE QUAY AS OUR BRAVE BOYS SAILED AWAY INTO BATTLE — DETERMINED THAT NO FOE SHOULD REACH OUR SHORES.

KEEP OFF ALL DISPLAYS

Unfortunately for Miss Bigger it seemed that one foe at least was still around. . .

'ERE, BLOOMIN' 'OOLIGAN! CAN'T YOU READ?

BUT I WAS MERELY TRYING TO INSTIL MY GIRLS WITH THE SPIRIT OF THOSE DAYS.

AND DON'T COME BACK! WE DON'T WANT YOUR SORT IN 'ERE!

DON'T LET THAT COMMON MONSTER UPSET YOU, GIRLS. WE'LL TAKE OUR CUSTOM ELSEWHERE.

AT LEAST WE DIDN'T HAVE TO LOOK AT THE REST OF THE RELICS.

SUE, PLEASE HELP ME. I WANT TO ENTER THAT BEAUTY CONTEST.

BEAUTY CONTEST at the TOWN HALL

WITH MISS BIGGER ABOUT? THE OLD SOUL WOULD THROW A FIT IF SHE EVEN NOTICED THE POSTERS!

IF I CAN WIN SOME MONEY I CAN TREAT MUM AND DAD. IT'S THEIR WEDDING ANNIVERSARY AT THE END OF THE MONTH.

OF COURSE I'LL HELP. YOU GET READY. I'LL PUT THE GIRLS IN THE PICTURE. WE'LL TAKE CARE OF THINGS AT THIS END.

FUNFAIR

VINTAGE CAR MUSEUM

I'LL JUST CHECK YOU'RE ALL HERE, DON'T WANT TO LOSE ANYONE, DO WE? NOW, STRONG, ROBBINS. . .

But . . .

. . .WELSH, STRONG. STRONG? WHAT ARE YOU DOING AT THIS END?

THIS END? DON'T KNOW WHAT YOU MEAN, MISS. I'VE ALWAYS BEEN AT THIS END, AIN'T I GIRLS?

I SHALL COUNT YOU AGAIN. NOW PLEASE KEEP STILL. STRONG, WELSH. . .

DEFINITELY, MISS.

ROBBINS, STRONG — AAAAH! OH DEAR — AHEM — MUST BE THE HEAT.

YOU ALL RIGHT, MISS? LOOK AS THOUGH YOU'VE BEEN SEEING THINGS. P'HAPS YOU SHOULD SIT DOWN IN THE SHADE FOR A BIT.

NONSENSE. I'M PERFECTLY ALL RIGHT. WE'LL MISS OUT THE VINTAGE CARS AND GO TO THE TOWN HALL. YOU'LL FIND IT HOLDS IMMENSE HISTORICAL INTEREST.

YEAH, BUT THAT ISN'T ALL IT HOLDS!

Fortunately for the girls, Miss Bigger seemed to get carried away suddenly.

PLEASE LET ME GET AWAY. I WISH TO GO TO THE TOWN HALL.

YOU COMIN' ON THE ROUNDABOUT WIV ME, LADY?

NOW SHE'S IN THE FUNFAIR, ALL WE'VE GOT TO DO IS MAKE SURE SHE STAYS HERE 'TILL CINDY GETS BACK.

IS THAT ALL? WELL, YOU ASK HER IF SHE'D LIKE A RIDE ON THE SWING-BOATS, 'COS I'M NOT!

MISS BIGGER, ARE YOU ALL RIGHT? COME ON, WE'LL FIND YOU SOMEWHERE NICE AND QUIET TO SIT DOWN.

WHAT A CONSIDERATE GIRL YOU ARE, STRONG. I DO FEEL EXTREMELY DAZED.

IS IT MUCH FARTHER?

NO, MISS, YOU'LL SOON BE ABLE TO HAVE A NICE QUIET SIT DOWN.

PAY THE FELLA QUICK, 'FORE SHE REALISES WHERE SHE'S GOIN'.

IT'S VERY DRAUGHTY ALL OF A SUDDEN. I'LL GO AND FIND SOMEWHERE A LITTLE WARMER TO — AAAAH!

HEY, SIT DOWN AN' STOP ROCKIN' THE BOAT!

WASN'T THAT SMASHIN', MISS? YOU'RE A GREAT SPORT.

I HATE HEIGHTS — CAN'T IMAGINE WHAT POSSESSED ME TO COME TO THIS DREADFUL PLACE.

The ride couldn't end quickly enough for Miss Bigger...

It turned out to be a really fantastic day...

ANIMAL MAGIC

BESSIE BUNTER

Just peep inside a work-box, needlecase, or sewing machine cabinet, and you're likely to find an ancient source of magic – in the shape of an ordinary pin!

POINT FOR PIN MAGIC!

This old belief dates back many hundreds of years, to the time when pins were made only of pure silver. Of course, we all know how valuable silver is today. But centuries ago, it was even more precious, because there were no proper mining processes and no way of producing any imitation of silver.

For a long time, the Moon had been looked upon as a magic sign of happiness, peace and good fortune. There were many charms and ancient spells for wishing on the Moon, its silvery sheen, and its calm, peaceful appearance in the night sky, free from the worries or cares of earth. And it wasn't long before silver became regarded as the magic Moon metal, and a symbol of all that was perfect.

But silver was mainly for the rich. The only piece of silver which an ordinary person could expect to own were pins, which most people kept for yearly pilgrimages to the Holy Shrines. Dotted along the pilgrimage routes were a number of wells, and the

custom was to throw one or two pins into one, in the hope of receiving a blessing, or having a prayer answered. Many of these wells remain to this day, especially in Wales, where visitors continue to offer pins as a gift to the water spirits of the well, or to the Saint to whom the well is dedicated.

This custom is just one reason why lots of people still believe: "See a pin, and pick it up And all day long, you'll have good luck!"

An extra pin meant an extra favour to ask at the next well. And an extra favour might mean a longed-for wish being granted!

In many parts of the world, a gift of pins is still thought to bring freedom from want and hunger for a newly-married couple, and, not so long ago, a young man might give his sweetheart pins as a token of his love.

"I'll give you a penny-worth of pins, for that's the way our loves begins. . ." are the first two lines of a traditional folk love-song.

As you probably know, there are many other sayings about pins. Almost every day, we hear somebody saying: "For two pins, I'd-" or "I don't care a row of pins!" And, if a lady does a spare-time job, lots of people still call her earnings "pin-money", meaning money which is supposed to be spent on little luxuries - which probably did include some pins in bygone days.

With pins being so important, it's not surprising that there are a number of charms connected with them. When a family moved into a new home, the head of the house-hold would often stick a pin into the gate-post or door frame, using just one jab.

If the pin fell out immediately, this was a sign that they could be on the move again before too long. If the pin dropped out after a few seconds, then the move would not be per-manent, but there would be happiness at the new home. If it stayed firm, this promised lasting success and content-ment, waiting through the door.

Girls stuck pins through candles to find out if their sweethearts were true. When the candle had burnt down past the pin, and if the pin had fallen out of the wick, the girl knew her boyfriend was false. But when a pin remained in the wick, all was well, and he would soon visit her to declare his love!

A pin dropping point-first, like a harpoon, into a mat or crack in the floorboard, was looked upon as an indication of a difficult task being done fairly easily, a problem solved, or an obstacle overcome relating to the place where it was dropped.

There is also a very old, but very simple means of fortune-telling by pins. Just lay one pin sideways on a table, and ask a question. Then give the pin a gentle push with one finger.

If the pin moves around in a circle, it will be the answer you want. If it shoots upwards, along the table, and stops suddenly, there will be some setbacks and disappointments before you get your wish. And a pin which stops with its point facing you means a lot of competition and opposition to your wish.

A pin making only part of a circle is a sign that you should make a little more effort to get what you want, but if the pin careers all over the place in no particular direction — well, it was probably a crazy idea, anyway!

THE FAIRGROUND OF FEAR

IT'S SO HOT TODAY. I'D LOVE TO GO OUT BUT FATHER IS SO STRICT. HE MAKES ME FEEL LIKE A PRISONER HERE.

It promised to be a lonely summer for Julie Whitland in the sleepy village of Baychurch. Julie had been adopted by Sir Edgar Whitland, a leading figure and large landowner in the village, who kept himself above the other villagers and expected the same of Julie . . .

WHAT'S THAT? SOUNDS LIKE MUSIC AND IT'S COMING THIS WAY. I MUST GO AND LOOK.

GOSH! IT'S A BRASS BAND!

. . AND A PROCESSION. A FAIRGROUND'S COME TO TOWN. IF ONLY I COULD GO TO IT!

The procession stopped . . .

THAT CLOWN LOOKS AS THOUGH HE'S DOING TRICKS JUST FOR ME.

OH, HOW LOVELY! HE WAS DOING THEM FOR ME! THANK YOU!

HERE — CATCH!

LUMME! WHAT'S THIS?

IT'S AN ADVERT FOR THE FAIRGROUND . . . AND AT THE BOTTOM — A MESSAGE FROM THAT GIRL. SHE WANTS ME TO MEET HER TOMORROW.

SHE LOOKS NICE. . .PERHAPS SHE WANTS TO BE MY FRIEND.

JULIE!

D-DAD! I THOUGHT YOU WERE OUT!

THAT'S OBVIOUS OR YOU WOULDN'T BE WATCHING THAT COMMON RUBBISH OUT THERE!

HE'S TAKING ME AWAY FROM THE SUNLIGHT AND LAUGHTER, LIKE HE ALWAYS DOES.

HOW MANY TIMES MUST I TELL YOU THAT YOU ARE DIFFERENT FROM OTHER PEOPLE — YOU ARE A WHITLAND!

THIS IS A PICTURE OF MY DAUGHTER, JULIE. WHEN SHE AND HER BABY DIED I ADOPTED YOU TO TAKE THEIR PLACE. SO I EXPECT YOU TO BEHAVE LIKE A WHITLAND!

WH-WHAT HAPPENED TO HER HUSBAND?

HE'S DEAD AND FORGOTTEN! NOW READ A BOOK IF YOU'RE BORED!

HE'S ANGRY WITH ME, BUT HE WON'T STOP ME ENJOYING MYSELF THIS TIME.

Late that night when her father was asleep . . .

THAT GIRL SAID TO MEET HER TOMORROW, BUT FATHER WON'T LET ME OUT THEN . . . I'LL HAVE TO GO THERE TONIGHT.

As Julie made her way to the fairground the sky darkened with a coming storm . . .

THAT SOUNDED LIKE THUNDER . . . I WAS STUPID COMING OUT TONIGHT.

Suddenly there was a flash of lightning . . .

AH! THERE'S THE FAIRGROUND! BUT I'M GOING TO GET SOAKED GETTING THERE.

THE PLACE IS DESERTED AND IT LOOKS SO EERIE. OH, I WISH I'D NEVER COME.

To Julie the fairground figures looked like gargoyles in the unreal light of the storm . . .

AAGH! H-HOW HORRIBLE!

IT — IT'S ALL SO SCAREY — I MUST GET AWAY.

OH, NO — I'VE TRIPPED!

THE HOUSE OF MEMORIES
THE PAST WILL COME ALIVE BEFORE YOUR VERY EYES

OH, DEAR, I'M BEING SILLY — IT'S ONLY A THUNDERSTORM, AFTER ALL. I THINK I'LL SHELTER IN THERE FROM THE RAIN...

LOOK WITHIN AND THE PAST WILL BE REVEALED

C-CRIKEY! THAT LOOKS LIKE A GIANT CRYSTAL BALL. WONDER WHAT IT IS..?

THERE SEEM TO BE SHAPES IN IT... SWIRLING SHAPES.

Then...

LUMME! IT — IT'S MY FATHER'S REAL DAUGHTER. THE ONE WHO DIED. AND SHE'S TRYING TO SAY SOMETHING.

JULIE... HEED MY FATHER! DO NOT MEDDLE... THE PAST MUST BE FORGOTTEN!

WHAT DOES SHE MEAN?

THE FAIRGROUND, JULIE... IT IS EVIL. YOU MUST GO... GO AWAY! NOW!

SHE'S GOING AWAY... BUT WHAT'S THAT — A SHADOW?

Julie whirled round...

OH! IT'S YOU! THE CLOWN FROM THE PROCESSION... YOU GAVE ME A FRIGHT!

B-BUT WHY ARE YOU LOOKING AT ME LIKE THAT? PLEASE DON'T... YOU'RE FRIGHTENING ME!

THE-THE FAIRGROUND CLOWN LOOKS SO DIFFERENT – SO EVIL. AND HIS EYES – THEY'RE MAKING ME FEEL DIZZY!

Later . . .

WH-WHERE AM I? WHO ARE YOU?

I'M CARLA – AND THIS IS MY FATHER, MISTER FRASER. HE LOOKS AFTER THE FAIRGROUND. YOU DO REMEMBER THE PROCESSION, DON'T YOU?

YES. YOU GAVE ME A NOTE ASKING ME TO MEET YOU.

YOU LOOKED SO LONELY. BUT I DIDN'T EXPECT YOU TO COME HERE IN THE MIDDLE OF THE NIGHT. THAT THUNDERSTORM MUST HAVE SCARED YOU. WE FOUND YOU LYING IN THE RAIN.

MY MIND SEEMS FUZZY BUT I'M SURE IT WASN'T JUST THE STORM THAT SCARED ME.

THE RAIN'S STOPPED NOW. I'LL SEE YOU HOME SINCE YOU'RE STILL SHAKY.

THAT CLOWN STANDING OVER THERE. . . THERE'S SOMETHING FAMILIAR ABOUT HIM BUT IT'S NO USE – I CAN'T REMEMBER.

SO YOU CAME TONIGHT BECAUSE YOUR FATHER DISAPPROVES OF FAIRGROUNDS. HOW STRANGE! I THOUGHT EVERYONE LOVED THEM.

HE'S NOT MY REAL FATHER. HE ADOPTED ME AS A BABY. BUT EVER SINCE I CAN REMEMBER HE'S TOLD ME I MUST HONOUR THE GREAT NAME OF WHITLAND.

I'VE HEARD HE OWNS MOST OF THE LAND ROUND HERE AND IS A BIT SNOBBISH ABOUT IT. BUT TRY TO COME TO THE FAIR TOMORROW. WE COULD HAVE A GREAT TIME.

I'LL TRY, CARLA. YOU'RE THE FIRST FRIEND I'VE EVER MADE.

Next morning . . .

JULIE, I'VE GOT TO GO OUT TODAY. BUT I'VE TOLD ANGELA HERE TO KEEP AN EYE ON YOU. I WON'T HAVE YOU GOING TO THAT FAIR!

FATHER MEANS WELL. IF ONLY HE DIDN'T THINK THERE'S NOTHING AND NO ONE GOOD ENOUGH FOR A WHITLAND.

THE HOUSE SEEMS EVEN MORE GLOOMY AND EMPTY TODAY THAN USUAL, ANGELA.

THAT'S 'COS ALL THE OTHER SERVANTS HAVE GONE TO THE FAIR, MISS.

YOU'D LIKE TO GO TOO, WOULDN'T YOU, ANGELA? WELL, WHY DON'T YOU? I WON'T TELL.

OH, MISS, I'D LOVE TO! BUT PROMISE ME YOU WON'T GO. I'LL GET INTO TERRIBLE TROUBLE IF YOU DO!

I PROMISE, ANGELA. I'LL JUST GO FOR A WALK – HONEST.

THE VILLAGE IS SO QUIET. LOOKS LIKE EVERYONE'S GONE TO THE FAIR BUT ME.

HELLO, JULIE!

IT'S THE MISS GRAYS GOING TO THE FAIR TOGETHER. THEY'RE INSEPARABLE, THE DEARS.

GOING TO THE FAIR AS WELL, DEAR? WELL, YOU CAN COME ALONG WITH US.

N-NO! I CAN'T GO!

NONSENSE! A YOUNG GIRL LIKE YOU WILL LOVE THE FAIR AND DON'T WORRY — WE PROMISE NOT TO TELL YOUR FATHER IF THAT'S WHAT'S WORRYING YOU.

I SUPPOSE IT WOULD BE ALL RIGHT JUST TO GO AND LOOK.

OH, IT'S SO WONDERFUL AND GAY. FUNNY, I SEEM TO HAVE A VAGUE MEMORY OF IT BEING CREEPY WHEN I CAME LAST NIGHT.

ENJOY YOURSELVES! I'M JUST GOING TO HAVE A LOOK AROUND.

WE'LL PROBABLY SCARE OURSELVES SILLY, WON'T WE, DEAR?

IT'S SO EXCITING! I COULD STAY HERE FOR EVER.

But then . . .

IT'S THAT CLOWN AGAIN!

I'VE GOT TO FIND OUT WHAT REALLY HAPPENED LAST NIGHT. SOMEHOW I'M SURE HE KNOWS.

PHEW! HE'S GOING SO QUICKLY. I CAN HARDLY KEEP UP WITH HIM.

OH, NO! I'VE LOST HIM, AND MYSELF BY THE LOOKS OF THINGS.

WHAT'S THAT? THE HOUSE OF MEMORIES! I WAS THERE LAST NIGHT. IT — IT'S COMING BACK TO ME.

Julie remembered a crystal globe and the face of her adopted father's real daughter who had died before Julie was adopted . . .

JULIE, GO AWAY. . . THIS PLACE IS EVIL. . . YOU MUST GO. . . GO !

Julie's reverie was suddenly shattered . . .

WHAT'S THAT COMMOTION ? SOUNDS LIKE A FIGHT !

TAKE THAT ! I HATE YOU !

GOOD GRIEF ! IT'S THE MISS GRAYS AND THEY'RE FIGHTING ! WHY, THEY'VE NEVER SAID A CROSS WORD TO EACH OTHER IN THEIR WHOLE LIVES !

I HATE YOU TOO, YOU OLD WITCH !

TAKE THAT, YOU PIG !

GOOD GRIEF ! THE WHOLE TRAIN'S GONE MAD. WHAT'S HAPPENED ?

I HATE YOU — HATE YOU !

I DON'T KNOW WHY I EVER GOT ENGAGED TO YOU, YOU CREEP !

CALL YOURSELF A FRIEND — YOU DOUBLE-DEALING OLD ROGUE !

I'M GOING TO THUMP YOU, YOU TOAD !

THE CLOWN ! NOW I REMEMBER. HE SCARED ME LAST NIGHT AND HE'S BEHIND THIS AS WELL. . . I CAN FEEL IT !

TAKE THAT, YOU OLD BAT !

OH, CARLA!

THOSE PEOPLE ON THE GHOST TRAIN... WHY ARE THEY ALL FIGHTING WITH ONE ANOTHER?

OH, JULIE, THANK GOODNESS I'VE FOUND YOU. YOU'VE GOT TO GET AWAY FROM HERE!

CARLA! WHAT IS IT? WHAT'S WRONG?

QUICK! GET BEHIND THIS CARAVAN! YOUR FATHER'S HERE!

YOU'D BETTER HIDE IN HERE.

I LEFT YOU IN CHARGE OF MY DAUGHTER. NOW I FIND YOU HERE. WHERE'S JULIE?

SHE ISN'T HERE, SIR. SHE PROMISED ME SHE WOULDN'T COME.

PHEW! THAT WAS CLOSE, CARLA, THOSE PEOPLE WHO WERE FIGHTING SEEM OKAY NOW. WHAT HAPPENED?

I'LL SHOW YOU, JULIE. BUT WE'D BETTER LIE LOW FOR A BIT.

Later...

THE CLOWN'S BEHIND IT ALL, ISN'T HE?

DON'T BE SILLY... COME ON, I'LL SHOW YOU WHAT MUST HAVE HAPPENED.

CLOSED

THIS IS THE GHOST TUNNEL, BUT THERE AREN'T ANY FAKE GHOSTS OR CREEPY SPIDERS... NOTHING EXCEPT A LOT OF MACHINES.

THAT'S RIGHT. WE'RE FULL OF TECHNICAL GADGETS. THIS ONE IS WHAT DAD CALLS A HALLUCINOGENIC MACHINE...

I DON'T KNOW HOW IT WORKS, BUT IT MAKES PEOPLE IMAGINE THEY SEE GHOSTS AND OTHER CREEPY THINGS. SOMETHING MUST HAVE GONE WRONG AND PEOPLE SAW EACH OTHER AS MONSTERS INSTEAD!

CRIKEY! SOUNDS SCIENCE FICTIONISH. BUT THAT WOULD EXPLAIN WHY THEY STARTED FIGHTING EACH OTHER.

HALLUCINATOR

BUZZZ

WHAT'S THAT NOISE, CARLA?

OH NO! IT'S THE MACHINERY — IT'S STARTED WORKING AGAIN. WE'D BETTER GET OUT FAST! IT HASN'T BEEN MENDED YET.

ZZZ

I CAN'T SEE PROPERLY. YOUR FACE, CARLA — IT LOOKS BLURRED.

DON'T LOOK AT ME, JULIE!

WHAT YOU'RE SEEING ISN'T REAL ANYMORE. JUST TAKE MY HAND AND RUN!

N — NO... STAY AWAY FROM ME. YOU'RE HORRIBLE — I HATE YOU!

I CAN'T HOLD OUT AGAINST THE MACHINE MUCH LONGER. PLEASE TRUST ME, JULIE. LOOK OUT BEHIND YOU!

OOOH!

Outside . . .

Later at Sir Whitland's . . .

IT'S ALMOST AS THOUGH EVERYONE WAS KEEPING A SECRET FROM ME. AND THAT FAIRGROUND IS THE KEY — I'M SURE OF IT.

WHAT A STRANGE THOUGHT TO HAVE. THAT BUMP ON THE HEAD IS MAKING ME FANCIFUL.

At the fairground . . .

GOOD AFTERNOON! I'M THE LOCAL MAGISTRATE IN BAYCHURCH. I'VE COME TO INSPECT THE FAIRGROUND AFTER A COMPLAINT FROM SIR WHITLAND.

WE'VE BEEN EXPECTING YOU. DO LET ME SHOW YOU AROUND.

I'VE HEARD SOME VERY DISQUIETING STORIES ABOUT YOUR FAIRGROUND. IF THEY PROVE CORRECT, I'M GOING TO HAVE TO CLOSE YOU DOWN.

I'M SURE I CAN PUT YOUR MIND AT REST — LET ME SHOW YOU THE HALL OF MIRRORS FIRST.

HALL of MIRRORS
EVERY ONE 'A LAUGH & EVERY

Later, at Sir Whitland's . . .

IT'S GETTING DARK AND THAT MAGISTRATE STILL HASN'T RETURNED. WHAT THE DEVIL'S KEEPING HIM?

At that moment in the Hall of Mirrors . . .

HELP ME! SOMEONE HELP ME . . . I'M TRAPPED! I — I CAN'T FIND A WAY OUT!

I'VE DEALT WITH THAT MAGISTRATE. I DON'T WANT ANYONE ELSE CREEPING ROUND TONIGHT : . . YOU KNOW WHAT TO DO.

YES.

FATHER SAYS THE FAIRGROUND WILL BE GONE BY TOMORROW. I MUST GO THERE TONIGHT ONE MORE TIME. I'VE GOT TO VISIT THAT HOUSE OF MEMORIES.

THE FAIRGROUND LOOKS SO CREEPY AT NIGHT. BUT I MUSTN'T BE AFRAID. I MUST REMEMBER WHY I'VE COME HERE. THERE'S THE HOUSE OF MEMORIES OVER THERE.

COME ON, CRYSTAL GLOBE — NO ONE WILL TELL ME WHO MY REAL PARENTS ARE. PLEASE SHOW ME. YOU — YOU SHOWED ME MY ADOPTED FATHER'S DEAD DAUGHTER BEFORE . . .

Figures appeared in the globe . . .

WHY, THAT'S SIR WHITLAND AND THE DOCTOR. THAT NURSE WHO'S HOLDING THE BABY LOOKS FAMILIAR, TOO.

I'LL ADOPT THIS CHILD AND CALL HER JULIE.

THE BABY — IT'S ME!

NO ONE BUT WE THREE MUST EVER KNOW WHO HER REAL PARENTS ARE.

But then the picture faded and in its place came a message . . .

YOU MUST FIND THE FAIRGROUND'S SECRET TO FIND YOURSELF

THE IMAGES HAVE GONE . . . HEY, WHAT DOES THAT MEAN?

Later, outside . . .

NO POINT THINKING ABOUT IT JUST NOW. I'D BETTER GET HOME BEFORE I'M MISSED . . . LUMME! WHAT'S THAT NOISE? SOUNDS LIKE SOME SORT OF ANIMAL.

GOOD GRIEF! IT — IT'S A TIGER — AND IT'S ON THE LOOSE.

I'D BETTER HIDE IN THIS CARAVAN TILL IT PASSES . . .

THOSE TIGERS YOU LEFT OUT THERE ARE ACTING UP. IT'S INSANE TO USE THEM AS WATCHDOGS. THEY COULD KILL SOMEONE.

THERE'S SOMEONE IN HERE.

IT'S MR. FRASER AND THE CLOWN.

SHUT UP! YOU'LL DO EXACTLY AS I SAY! WE'VE GOT A BUSY DAY AHEAD OF US TOMORROW. WHAT YOU MIGHT CALL A GREY DAY... HA! HA! NOW LET'S HAVE A LOOK AT THOSE TIGERS.

BUT MR. FRASER OWNS THE FAIRGROUND DOESN'T HE? SO WHY WAS THAT CLOWN BOSSING HIM AROUND? THERE SEEMS TO BE SO MUCH I DON'T UNDERSTAND ABOUT THIS FAIRGROUND.

OOPS! SOMEONE'S COMING BACK. I'LL HAVE TO RISK THOSE TIGERS AND MAKE A DASH FOR IT.

Scared out of her wits, Julie ran all the way home...

THAT PLACE — IT'S A REAL NIGHTMARE. WHY WOULD ANYONE WANT TIGERS PATROLLING THE FAIRGROUND? WHAT HAVE THEY GOT TO HIDE?

Next morning...

FATHER, DID DOCTOR PEARSON EVER HAVE A NURSE?

YES! I THOUGHT YOU KNEW. SHE WAS ONE OF THE MISS GREYS... EDNA, I BELIEVE.

OF COURSE! THAT'S WHO IT IS! THAT'S WHY SHE SEEMED FAMILIAR!

Later...

I'M AFRAID WE CAN'T FIND THE MAGISTRATE, SIR. WE SEARCHED THE WHOLE FAIRGROUND. THEY SAY HE NEVER SHOWED UP.

BLAST! THAT MEANS WE CAN'T SHUT THE PLACE DOWN.

FATHER'S BEEN WATCHING ME LIKE A HAWK ALL DAY. NOW'S MY CHANCE TO SLIP OFF AND SEE MISS GREY.

NO POINT IN YOU RINGING THAT BELL, DEARIE. THE MISS GREYS HAVE BEEN AT THE FAIRGROUND SINCE BREAKFAST TIME. DAFT ABOUT IT THEY ARE!

YOU'D THINK AT THEIR AGE THEY'D HAVE MORE SENSE! BUT THE WHOLE VILLAGE SEEMS TO HAVE GONE NUTS ABOUT IT!

I'VE BEEN SEARCHING FOR AGES BUT I CAN'T SEE THEM ANYWHERE. THE PLACE IS PACKED OUT.

THERE'S CARLA — MR. FRASER'S DAUGHTER. PERHAPS SHE CAN HELP ME! WE'RE GOOD FRIENDS.

JULIE — FANTASTIC!

OH, NO — CARLA'S WITH HER FATHER AND THE CLOWN.

HELLO, JULIE! HOW ARE YOU?

I — I'M FINE THANK YOU, MR. FRASER. I WAS LOOKING FOR THE TWO MISS GREYS. HAVE YOU SEEN THEM?

YES . . . I — I'M AFRAID I HAVE. ARE THEY FRIENDS OF YOURS?

YES! HAS SOMETHING HAPPENED TO THEM?

WELL, THERE'S BEEN AN UNFORTUNATE LITTLE INCIDENT CONCERNING ONE OF THEM . . . MISS EDNA. SHE'S BEEN ARRESTED FOR PICKPOCKETING.

PICKPOCKETING? MISS EDNA? THAT'S IMPOSSIBLE! SHE'D NEVER DREAM OF STEALING ANYTHING!

SHE HANDED HERSELF IN AT THE POLICE STATION ALONG WITH ALL THE VALUABLES SHE'D STOLEN. SHE ADMITTED EVERYTHING!

BUT THAT DOESN'T MAKE SENSE. AND THERE'S SOMETHING ABOUT THAT CLOWN — SOMETHING HE SAID LAST NIGHT. IT'S NIGGLING AT THE BACK OF MY MIND.

Then Julie remembered . . .

WE'VE GOT A BUSY DAY AHEAD OF US TOMORROW. WHAT YOU MIGHT CALL A GREY DAY. HA! HA!

THAT WAS IT — A GREY DAY! HE DID THIS TO MISS EDNA GREY. B — BUT HOW? FOR WHAT REASON? WHY DID HE CHOOSE THE ONE PERSON WHO MIGHT TELL ME ABOUT MY PARENTS? THE HOUSE OF MEMORIES IS RIGHT — I MUST FIND THE FAIRGROUND'S SECRET TO FIND MYSELF!

THE HOUSE OF MEMORIES SAID I MUST FIND THE SECRET BEHIND THE FAIRGROUND TO FIND WHO I REALLY AM.

NOW MISS GRAY WHO MIGHT HAVE TOLD ME WHO MY REAL PARENTS WERE HAS BEEN ARRESTED FOR PICKPOCKETING AT THIS FAIR. I MUST GO AND SEE HER.

But at the police station . . .

THERE SHE IS, MISS. BUT IT WON'T DO YOU MUCH GOOD TRYING TO TALK TO HER. ALL SHE MANAGES TO SAY IS THAT IT WAS HER THAT DID THE PICKPOCKETING. A BIT LOONY IF YOU ASK ME.

Julie talked to the other Miss Gray . . .

WHAT HAPPENED TO YOUR SISTER, MISS GRAY? PLEASE TELL ME ABOUT IT.

I-I DON'T KNOW WHAT HAPPENED. EDNA WOULD NEVER STEAL. WE'D JUST GONE TO THE FAIR FOR THE DAY . . .

WE SAW THIS SIDE SHOW CALLED THE MYSTERIOUS MESMAN. IT LOOKED LIKE GOOD FUN.

MESMAN THE MAGICIAN THE GREATEST HYPNOTIST IN THE WORLD

NOW I WOULD LIKE A VOLUNTEER FROM THE AUDIENCE. HOW ABOUT YOU, LADY?

WHO . . . ME? OH DEAR? WELL, I SUPPOSE IT WILL BE A BIT OF A LARK.

THE SUBJECT HAS NOW BEEN HYPNOTISED. SHE WILL BELIEVE ANYTHING I TELL HER ABOUT HERSELF AND WILL DO EXACTLY AS I SAY.

"MESMAN TOLD HER THAT SHE WAS A GREAT BALLET DANCER AND MUST DANCE FOR THE AUDIENCE . . ."

HE'S MAKING FUN OF EDNA . . . THAT'S NOT FAIR.

"THEN THE CURTAIN CLOSED AND I DIDN'T SEE EDNA AGAIN TILL I CAME OUTSIDE. SHE SEEMED HER USUAL SELF AGAIN . . ."

JESSICA! HERE I AM! HERE I AM. WHAT HAPPENED? WHAT DID I DO?

BUT LATER I LOST HER IN THE CROWD AND THE NEXT THING I KNEW SHE'D BEEN ARRESTED FOR PICKPOCKETING.

MESMAN COULD HAVE MADE HER STEAL. HE SAID HE COULD MAKE HER DO ANYTHING.

Julie went straight to the fair . . .

THIS SHOW. . . WHY ARE YOU CLOSING IT?

DON'T ASK ME. I'M ONLY FOLLOWING ORDERS. SEEMS IT WAS ONLY OPEN FOR ONE SPECIAL PERFORMANCE.

MESMAN THE M—
CLOSED
—EST —NOTIST — WORLD

A SPECIAL PERFORMANCE TO GET MISS GRAY? BUT WHY? AND WHERE'S THE CLOWN? HE'S ALWAYS LURKING ABOUT – UP TO NO GOOD.

HI, THERE, JULIE! YOU'RE LOOKING VERY THOUGHTFUL.

OH, CARLA. . . AM I GLAD TO SEE YOU!

Julie told her of her suspicions about the fairground . . .

YOU THINK THAT OUR FAIRGROUND IS OUT TO GET PEOPLE IN THIS VILLAGE? HAVE YOU LOST YOUR SENSES?

IT'S TRUE, CARLA. FIRST THE MAGISTRATE DISAPPEARS, THEN MISS GRAY STEALS. AND YOUR FATHER'S IN ON IT. I HEARD THE CLOWN TELL HIM HE MUST DO EXACTLY AS HE SAYS!

MY FATHER! YOU HAVE GONE MAD! HE'S RUN THIS FAIR NEARLY ALL HIS LIFE AND NO ONE'S EVER SAID A WORD AGAINST HIM. JUST WHO DO YOU THINK YOU ARE?

A WHITLAND! THAT'S WHO SHE THINKS SHE IS. WE CALL THEM THE SNOBS ON THE HILL!

CARLA, PLEASE. .

YOU'RE MY FRIEND, CARLA. . .

WAS YOUR FRIEND! PEOPLE WARNED ME THAT YOU THOUGHT YOU WERE TOO GOOD FOR ANY-ONE. THEY WERE RIGHT!

GO ON! RUN AWAY TO YOUR BIG HOUSE! THAT'S WHERE YOU WHITLANDS BELONG. . . AND DON'T BOTHER COMING BACK HERE!

THAT'S SHOWN THE SNOB!

2
SH

4p
ALL PR
TO BE

I-I'M NOT A SNOB. MY FATHER WOULD NEVER LET ME PLAY WITH THE OTHER CHILDREN. C-CARLA WAS THE FIRST FRIEND I'D EVER HAD AND I'VE LOST HER.

IS THAT YOU, JULIE? PLEASE DON'T SLAM THE DOOR LIKE THAT. IT'S MOST UNCOUTH AND THAT IS SOMETHING A WHITLAND MUST NEVER BE.

HE DOESN'T CARE HOW UNHAPPY I AM. JUST SO LONG AS I BEHAVE LIKE A WHITLAND SHOULD!

Julie couldn't sleep that night . . .

IT WAS WRONG OF ME TO ACCUSE CARLA'S FATHER LIKE THAT. AFTER ALL, THE CLOWN COULD BE BLACKMAILING HIM. I WOULDN'T PUT ANYTHING PAST THAT — THAT MONSTER !

Suddenly, Julie heard a noise . .

THERE'S SOMEONE OUT THERE !

IT'S CARLA. . .SHE WANTS ME TO GO WITH HER. SHE MUST HAVE FORGIVEN ME.

THAT'S STRANGE. SHE HASN'T SPOKEN A WORD — BUT SHE WANTS ME TO FOLLOW HER.

CARLA'S BROUGHT ME TO THE FAIR . . .

SHE'S GONE INTO THE HALL OF MIRRORS. I MUSTN'T LOSE HER.

OH, NO ! CARLA'S GONE. . .AND-AND ALL THESE MIRRORS — MAKE EVERYTHING SO CONFUSING. I'M NOT SURE I CAN FIND MY WAY OUT. . .

PERHAPS CARLA'S ROUND HERE. . .OH, NO ! IT-IT'S THE CLOWN !

HA, HA ! HA, HA !

HE'S EVERYWHERE AND I CAN'T TELL WHICH IS THE REAL ONE. I'VE GOT TO GET OUT OF HERE. BUT HOW ? I CAN'T FIND THE EXIT ! I-I'M TRAPPED !

CARLA CAME INTO THE HALL OF MIRRORS — BUT SHE'S VANISHED!

I'M SURE THE CLOWN'S AT THE BOTTOM OF ALL THIS!

OW! I DON'T KNOW WHICH WAY TO GO. CARLA! WHERE ARE YOU? HELP ME!

IT'S NO USE SHOUTING. CARLA ISN'T HERE AND NEVER WAS.

YOU'RE LYING! I-I SAW HER!

WHAT YOU SAW WAS ONLY AN IMAGE OF HER PROJECTED BY THIS LITTLE MACHINE...LIKE THIS!

CARLA!

WHAT? MY HANDS HAVE GONE RIGHT THROUGH HER!

THAT'S BECAUSE THIS ISN'T HER. CARLA'S REALLY FAST ASLEEP IN HER CARAVAN.

I USED HER IMAGE TO LURE YOU HERE. YOU SEE, I NEED YOUR HELP. IT CONCERNS YOUR FATHER, SIR EDGAR.

N-NO, I WON'T HELP YOU. YOU WERE RESPONSIBLE FOR GETTING POOR MISS GREY JAILED FOR PICKPOCKETING!

BUT YOU WILL HELP, MY DEAR...YOU'VE NO CHOICE!

HIS EYES... THEY'RE SO HYPNOTIC. EVERYTHING'S GOING HAZY...

Next morning . . .

DID YOU WAKE JULIE? SHE'S LATE FOR BREAKFAST AND I CAN'T STAND UNTIMELINESS.

SIR EDGAR, S-SHE ISN'T IN HER ROOM. I CAN'T FIND HER ANYWHERE!

CONTINUED ON PAGE 97

ANIMAL MAGIC

A Santa for Sophie

It was going to be a Christmas to remember — that much was certain. Snow had fallen all week and now lay thick and even, turning the busy streets into a world of white silence. Mr. Bristow had managed to get the greenest, bushiest Christmas tree ever, along with the brightest, shiniest decorations and balloons imaginable and, on Christmas Eve, it was time for the yearly ritual. The trip to Harnsworth's, the town's big department store, to visit Santa Claus in his cave.

Since they had been tiny tots, Bob Bristow's eldest daughters — Angela and Marion — had called at Santa's grotto once a year.

Sitting on the merry old man's knee, they would tell him all the news of the year, about their parents and friends, and of course, what they really longed to receive as yule-tide presents. Even though they were older and knew that "Santa" was in reality old Mr. Drewson from Bates Street, they still looked forward to their annual visit — now taking their youngest sister, Sophie, to his magical cave of Christmas cheer.

But this year it was to be different. A year to remember, all right. The year the ritual had to stop!

"What? Christmas isn't Christmas without a visit to Santa's cave! You're joking, surely?" Angela Bristow

shot a horrified look at the graven-faced store manager.

"I just wish I was," replied the latter, shaking his head. "But old Mr. Drewson isn't at all well. I've been unable to find a replacement at short notice. So, as of two days ago, Santa's cave is closed."

"Oh, no! What will our Sophie say about that?" said Angela worriedly glancing across the store at her youngest sister, who was visible some little way off, a diminutive, excited figure, bustling along the gangway between rows of children's toys and dolls. "She really believes in Santa. Meeting him at the store is the high spot of the build-up to Christmas." How could they tell her the news?

"Perhaps it's time she learned the truth about 'Father Christmas', then," suggested ten-year-old Marion Bristow, with a sigh. "She's seven years old, after all. Shall we tell her that it's Mum and Dad who put the presents under the Christmas tree, and not a jolly-faced reindeer-driver at all?"

"Don't you dare, Marion," admonished her sister. "Christmas and Santa go hand in hand, when you're a kiddie. A touch of festive magic — as you should very well know," she continued. "It isn't so very long since you stopped writing notes for Father Christmas and pinning them up all over the house."

At that moment, conversation was interrupted by a rushing whirlwind of golden hair and excited eyes. Sophie was in their midst. Her shrill little voice jabbered at them. "Come on, Angela. Come on, Marion. Stop yakking. Take me to see Santa. I've masses to tell him . . . all about the year we've had . . . and what I've done at school . . . and about Aunt Bessie's new puppy . . . and-and what I'd like him to bring me tomorrow and, oh, come on! I can't wait any longer!"

"Hold on, Sophie. We've some bad news. It's about Santa . . ." Slowly, uncertainly, Angela told her little sister that poor Father Christmas was unwell and so she wouldn't be able to see him that year.

At once, tears sprang from disbelieving eyes. "You're teasing me, aren't you, Angela . . . Marion? Of course I'm going to see Santa. I've always visited him. Don't be so cruel."

What could the girls do but lead Sophie along the narrow passageway running from the main sales floor and into the cave. There were the walls, decorated, as every year, with painted reindeers, elves and pixies. There was the red silk chair Santa had sat upon for so many years. There was his big gift-sack, now laying screwed up on the floor, obviously empty. A big, black sign hung from the ceiling: SANTA'S CAVE — CLOSED!

"See? We told you, Sophie," muttered Marion, more upset than she cared to mention. "There's nothing for you here, we might as well go home."

On their return journey, Sophie's spirits revived somewhat. "Father Christmas **will** find a way to see me, you know. He doesn't have my list of presents, so how can he know what to bring me on Christmas Day?"

Marion opened her mouth as if to say something, but, glancing at Angela, thought better of it and remained silent all the way home. Back at 35, Mulberry Avenue, Angela took her parents to one side and told them the news. Bob Bristow nodded grimly, "Mr. Drewson must be eighty if he's a day. And all those years sitting in a draughty 'cave' can't have helped his health. I'm not really surprised that he's unwell . . . probably should have retired ages ago."

"But, Bob, he's a part of Christmas around here," Marjorie Bristow disagreed. "Why, he was the store Santa at Harnsworth's when you and I were tots. He knows all about us, about generations of local families."

"Well, he knows all about Sophie, anyway," remarked Marion, who had just walked into the room alone. "She never stops chattering, once she's sat on his knee. It's as if she saves up all the news, all the gossip for that once-a-year chinwag. But this year . . ." she trailed off then started again. "I did ask Angela if it might not be kinder to tell Sophie the truth about Santa, but . . ." She fell silent again, as did her sister and parents.

In each mind, was fixed memories of the Harnsworth's Santa. The merry eyes, all but hidden by white hair and waist-length false beard that curled all down his holly-berry-red cloak. Yes, their store Santa was the classic Father Christmas, perfect in every way. Only this year, his yule-tide cheer was missing. It was as if a slice of joy had been cut from the Christmas cake.

Bob was the first to break the silence, speaking to Marjorie in a voice held deliberately low so it would not carry into the adjoining room where little Sophie sat gazing into the blazing fire. "Mr. Drewson's house isn't far from here. I'll just pop down to see how he is. Wish him a merry Christmas. It can't be much fun for him, feeling out of sorts at the high point of his year."

With Mr. Bristow gone, the others sat down to tea. Usually, the chatter would have reached fever pitch over the mince pies and sausage rolls. Everything was ready, after all. The perfect setting for the day to come. The yule-log spluttered and crackled cheerily in the hearth, sending shivers of orange light into the furthest shadows.

The bright-coloured baubles hanging from the Christmas tree were caught in the glow, reflecting the flames in shades of magenta, purple and crimson, as they twisted and swayed in the fire's heat.

But the tea remained all but untouched, each girl thinking back to her childhood, with little Sophie, most upset of all; occasional, half-stifled sobs escaping from her tight-pressed lips.

After tea, Angela and Marion took Sophie aside to try and cheer her up with some yuletide guessing games. Their mother was washing up the dishes in the kitchen when Bob Bristow came in. One look at his set face told Mrs. Bristow the worst.

"It's bad, Marjie. Very bad. Worse than I thought! Mr. Drewson's daughter was there when I called. The old man ... well, he's not conscious. Apparently, he contracted a chill over a week ago, but still went 'on duty'. At his age, it knocked him right down. He's weak, slowly fading away. She says it's doubtful that he'll last the night."

Marjorie Bristow was appalled. "That's awful! That poor, kind old man, dying ... dying on Christmas Eve, at the time of year that meant so much to him ... and to all the children hereabouts. It's unjust — cruel ..."

What could they do? Mr. and Mrs. Bristow kept quiet about the news to avoid upsetting their daughters still more. They tried to jolly the evening along with games of 'Hunt the Slipper', 'Blind Man's Buff' and 'Sardines'. Angela and Marion joined in, moodily silent. They were more affected by the absence of the store Santa than they cared to admit. If they had known the whole truth, Christmas would have dissolved in floods of tears and heart-break. Bob Bristow was quite sure of that.

Sophie? Sophie kept to herself, staring mutely into the writhing flames of the fire. Her thoughts raced back over her few years to Christmases past, when Santa had always been there at the store to greet her, smile, and listen as she jabbered out her life story.

Fragments of conversations ...

"Yes, Sophie, of course I won't forget to visit you tonight". Note to Santa: A special extra dollop of Christmas cheer to 35, Mulberry Avenue ...

"Don't you ever get cold, Santa? Climbing in and out of houses in the frost and snow?"

"Cold? Well, I'll let you into a secret, little Sophie. If I see a house that has lots and lots of hot mince pies, well, crafty old Santa samples just one or two, mind, just to see if they're tasty enough for all my children!"

That remark had prompted Sophie to ask her mother to cook an extra dozen mince pies, which she resolutely left out every year, warming on a plate in the hearth. She'd have been horrified to learn that these were always scoffed by her elder sisters soon after she'd been consigned to bed.

This year — even if he wasn't well — he'd come! She knew it deep inside. So the pies had to be there, as always ...

"Come on, bed, you three." Her father's gruff voice interrupted her thoughts. "We've a long day ahead."

Yawning, Angela and Marion made their way towards the stairs. Only the pale, pinched face of Sophie remained, set in defiance.

"No, Daddy, I want to stay down here. Santa always leaves the presents under the tree, so I'm going to wait by the fire and wish him a merry Christmas when he comes, like I've wished him every year."

"Now, just a minute, my girl ..." Bob Bristow started, but felt a hand lightly touch his arm. "Leave her be, Bob," whispered his wife. "Not seeing Santa at the store's taken some of the magic of Christmas away from Sophie. Let her stay ... she'll soon fall asleep, and it's warm enough down here!"

An hour later, the house was asleep, waiting for the big day to dawn. Only the restless eyes of Sophie Bristow burned in the shadowy room. Snuggled on the sofa, a thick blanket wrapped around her warm nightdress, she waited for the Santa she loved ... for the Santa she knew would never forget her.

The room seemed strange, so dark, devoid of people. The only life burned in the hearth, its fiery reflection shimmering through the shadows, lighting the baubles on the tree as they slowly revolved in the warmth.

Baubles; moving, circling round and round, yellow, mauve, gold ... their colours catching her eye time and time again as she kept her lonely vigil. Somewhere, a clock chimed twelve times — midnight! Still the fire crackled. Still the only

sounds were the creaking of house timbers, the deafening hush of winter silence.

What was that? Distant sleigh bells ...? No, just a breeze-blown twig scratching at the window pane. Stubborn determination battled with Sophie's growing impatience. "He'll come, as he does every year. Even though I haven't wished him a merry Christmas, or given him my present list."

The girl was tired and, yes, a little hungry. The mince pies near the fire looked more and more delicious every moment. But ... "No! They're for Santa. I put them there every year and each time they're all gone by morning. He must really love them!"

Idly, her tired eyes wandered back to the tree and the nearest and brightest hanging bauble. A brilliant maroon, she could see the room reflected in it, lit up by the fire. There, distorted by the bauble's shape was her own face, the couch, beyond the cabinet, the TV set, the door. Wait! Was it just the swaying of the bauble or had the door moved? It seemed to be opening. In a second, she was wide awake, whirling her head away from the tree. What followed remained forever etched in her memory.

The door was indeed open. A figure stood there. A jolly, fat figure, a kindly, bearded face. Beside the figure a huge, bulging sack. It was HIM! "Santa! Santa!" Sophie leapt off the chair and rushed towards the newcomer, the words tripping over each other as they rushed from her mouth. "They said you weren't well, that I couldn't see you to wish you a Happy Christmas, but I knew I would if I stayed down here. I knew you wouldn't forget me ... or the other children!"

"Sophie Bristow, you really should be in bed." The familiar voice seemed a little strained. "But I'm glad you're not ... delivering presents can be a lonely job, especially when I've been, well, not quite myself, you could say."

Sophie was immediately all contrition. "Oh, you poor old Santa. Come and rest by the fire. You must be tired, lugging all those presents about. See, I've mince pies for you ... and a flask of hot soup."

Soon, Sophie was snuggled down on the sofa side-by-side with Santa ... chatting just as they would have done on Christmas Eve in the department store. "Brrr," she shivered, "your coat's icy cold. You must be freezing, out and about on a night like this."

"Cold?" chuckled her bearded companion, pouring himself a mug of soup. "How could Santa possibly be cold with all this Christmas cheer around him?" "Now," he went on, in a more serious vein. "Have you your present list? I hope I've got the right gifts in my sack."

Sophie had forgotten all about presents. "Oh, yes, Santa," she beamed, "I worked out what I wanted with Mummy and Daddy. But of course, I don't mind what I get, really. Just meeting you is the best thing about Christmas."

Not to be outdone, Santa smiled, "And, seeing your smiling face has made me feel a lot better, too, Sophie. Puts new strength and warmth into my old bones." Brushing the crumbs from his beard, he went on, "That and the mince pies, of course. Santa's rather partial to those."

"I know," beamed the little girl. "So they're all for you ... although ... although I might just try **one**." Soon, a regular feast was going on, the old man and the young girl tucking happily into a plateful of Christmas cheer. Afterwards came the time for talk. Sophie was ever-curious.

"I-I've often wondered, Santa," she began, "how you manage to get presents to all the boys and girls in the world in one night."

"Ah, that would be telling," came the reply. "But when they have to, my reindeers can move with the speed of light. Mind you, all this supersonic travel does take it out of you!"

"Did I ever tell you," he said, hurriedly changing the subject, "of the time I was visiting a little boy in Greenland? Home territory to me. Well, I got stuck in the smoke-hole of the igloo ... and my beard froze to the ice. They had to chip it off my chin with an ice-pick, then sew it back on when the thaw came. I was beardless for months.''

"Yes," piped Sophie, her memory evergreen. "You told me that tale the year before last, when I visited the store. Marion said you were fibbing, but I told her straight ... Santa Claus doesn't tell lies!"

The old man's grey eyes clouded. "No, I don't, usually," he muttered. "So I won't lie to you and say I'll see you next year. You see, I'm getting too old for this game. Very soon now, I'll be going away on a long, long journey ... and I won't ever be coming back." He looked sadly at his young companion as if asking for silent acceptance. It was not forthcoming.

After the initial shock, Sophie thrust an indignant face towards him, "You mean to retire? Well ... well you can't, and that's that. All the children in the neighbourhood know you, love you. Where would they be if there was no Santa at the store to talk to. No one to discuss presents with?"

Then Santa began to protest. "But, Sophie, a younger Santa will step into my shoes ..." He couldn't have said a worse thing. "We don't want a young Santa. Santas are supposed to be old. Why, you'd need to be a hundred years old at least to know all the boys and girls in the world. It stands to reason ..."

Suddenly, her anger turned to tears, burying her face in his white beard, she sobbed, "Oh, please ... please change your mind. Say you'll come back next year ... and every year. No one can take your place. You're special to the children ... they all rely on you ..."

The figure by her side stirred uneasily. "You mean that, do you? You think I'm special to all the children

around here ... that they rely on me?"

"Yes," hissed Sophie. "It isn't good enough, Santa. You can't go away and leave all your young friends. Without your smiling face, your jolly beard and red cloak welcoming us into your cave at the store, Christmas wouldn't ... wouldn't be anything at all ..." she finished lamely.

But her words had been enough. Now Santa was on his feet, pacing up and down in front of the fire. His face aglow with determination.

"Too old ... fiddlesticks! You're right, young Sophie. This is an old man's job. They can't keep a good Santa down. Don't worry, I won't retire for ages and ages. Of course I'll see you next year and the year after, and the year after ..."

Suddenly, his voice seemed to swell, to fill the whole room — "MERRY

CHRISTMAS" — a shout that sent the windows rattling. Next moment, Santa was gone. The door didn't seem to have opened. He just wasn't there. But a pile of presents was there, under the tree where she'd found them every Christmas morning that she could remember.

Happily, Sophie sank back on to the sofa, her eyes gazing dreamily at the Christmas tree baubles that swung and swayed, back and forth ... to and fro ... to and fro ...

"Hey, wake up!" Her father's voice. It was daylight. "It's gone ten o'clock, sleepy head, and you've been down here all night."

Her mother came towards her, smiling. "You were fast asleep, it seemed such a shame to wake you when we came ..." Quickly, Marjorie checked herself. She'd been about to add the words "down with the presents",

80

but little Sophie was too excited to notice her near slip-up.

"Asleep? I haven't been asleep, not for so long, anyway. Santa came and brought the presents. Listen ..." Smiling tolerantly, her father sat down next to Sophie while she gabbled on about the first ever time she'd met Santa in her own home.

Marion came into the room, to hear the last of her story. "You were dreaming, Sophie. No one ever sees Santa on Christmas Day."

Her disbelieving voice brought an instant response from her little sister. "Dreaming? Dreaming, was I? Look ... all the mince pies have gone, **and** the soup. We finished them off together. And ... there's something else ..." She screwed up her face trying to remember as her father, smiling, walked from the room. "Yes, Santa said he was going to retire. To go on a long, long journey, and never ever come back. But I stopped him. I told him he jolly well had to stay here and meet all the boys and girls at the store, as well as give out the presents, or else make everyone unhappy. It's thanks to me that Santa will be sticking around for years and years to come."

She stopped, breathing heavily. Even the normally tolerant Angela couldn't resist this. "You really were dreaming, weren't you, Tich? Might as well admit it!"

Before Sophie could retort, the girls' father came thoughtfully back into the room. "You know, someone did come here last night. There are wet footprints in the hall, and outside, boot-marks in the snow leading out onto the road."

"See, I told you! I told

you!" chanted Sophie. But before any further discussion could take place, there was a ring at the front door-bell. Mr. Bristow went to the summons.

There on the doorstep stood a middle-aged woman pushing a wheelchair, the occupant of which was all but hidden beneath layer upon layer of coats and blankets. Two bright, sparkling eyes were all that was visible of his face above a thick scarf and below a woolly hat.

"Miss Drewson!" Bob Bristow gasped "What are you doing here? And this isn't, isn't ..."

"Old Mr. Drewson?" the wrapped figure chimed in, "Yes, of course it's me. My daughter told me you called last night, and naturally I was unhappy about not seeing the boys and girls at the store, so I've come to wish one and all a Merry Christmas."

Inside the hall, the scarf and hat were removed to reveal the well-known features of the old man. Thin and grey-skinned ... his face hairless ... his head completely bald. His daughter wheeled him into the front room where the girls and their mother were opening Christmas presents. The door closed behind them, leaving Bob Bristow wondering. When he'd visited the night before, he'd been told that old Mr. Drewson had been at death's door. Now ...

The old man's daughter returned alone into the hall. She was obviously agitated. "It's incredible," she murmered. "Last night, I'd given up all hope. He was fading fast, but suddenly, just after midnight ... he seemed to change. Still asleep, he was smiling and happy. Kept speaking a name over and over again. Sophie ... that was the name ... as if he was talking to her, dreaming in

his sleep. We thought it was delirium, that the end was near, but he went from strength to strength. This morning found him sitting up, bright as a jewel, clamouring to be pushed around the town to see the families he'd known for so long as the store Santa Claus."

Wondering, Mr. Bristow looked into the front room. There was old Mr. Drewson, piping merry Christmas greetings to Marjorie and the girls. Angela and Marion speaking guardedly — they knew who Mr. Drewson really was. Little Sophie, friendly, polite, but no more. She little dreamed that this thin, grey, bald-headed old man was the fat, jolly, bearded Santa who had meant so much to her on Christmas Eve.

Minutes later, Miss Drewson was wheeling the old man back out of the front door. As he passed Bob Bristow, the latter looked up at him with keen, clear eyes. "I thought I was on the way out, Mr. Bristow, last night. You know what pulled me through? Little Sophie. I seemed to see her loving, trusting face and hear her happy chatter as I'd done each year since she was a toddler. "I knew that I couldn't just let myself go under, give up the struggle to live. I knew I'd be letting her down; and I couldn't do that."

Mr. Drewson made a sign for his daughter to push him out of the front door, then, as an afterthought, he leaned back in the chair and looked full into the eyes of Bob Bristow.

"Yes, your daughter pulled me though, Mr. Bristow. Her, and one thing more ... **those mince pies. Please tell your wife they were the finest I have ever tasted!"**

The End

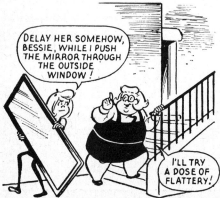

STATUE OF LIBERTY

THIS WORLD-FAMOUS STATUE IS A SYMBOL OF LIBERTY, AND IT CERTAINLY PROVED SO FOR JILL BEDLOW, DAUGHTER OF A RICH AMERICAN EMBASSY OFFICIAL IN LONDON.

THE STRANGE STORY

WELL, HONEY, MOM AND I ARE OFF TO THE STATES FOR THE 4TH JULY INDEPENDENCE CELEBRATIONS. STILL SURE YOU WON'T COME?

QUITE SURE, POP.

BUT JULY 4TH IS YOUR BIRTHDAY TOO, JILL. WE'D MAKE IT A SWELL OCCASION.

I KNOW, MOM. BUT IT'S QUITE IMPOSSIBLE.

I'VE GOT IMPORTANT EXAMS ON THAT DAY. I'VE STUDIED HARD ALL TERM FOR THEM AND I CAN'T WASTE ALL THAT EFFORT!

A week later at Jill's boarding school . . .

IT'S A BIRTHDAY PARCEL FROM AMERICA, JILL! GO ON — OPEN IT!

NO! IT SAYS NOT TO OPEN TILL JULY 4TH, AND THAT'S TOMORROW.

I WANT TO OPEN THIS MYSTERY PARCEL ON MY OWN, SO I'LL GET UP REAL EARLY TOMORROW.

Next morning . . .

I'LL GO TO MY FAVOURITE QUIET SPOT NEAR THE POOL.

HEY, BADGER — LOOK! IT'S THE BEDLOW GIRL 'ERSELF!

I TOLD YOU WATCHIN' THIS PLACE WOULD PAY OFF!

NICE 'N' EASY, KID! NO NOISE AN' YOU WON'T GET HURT!

UUGH!

TUCK-IN
with Tammy

Christmas Greetings

Marzipan Logs

Makes 12

Ingredients:
(Imperial)

2oz marzipan
1oz plain chocolate
Chocolate vermicelli

Metric

50g marzipan
25g plain chocolate
Chocolate vermicelli

1. If the marzipan is too hard, knead it a little to make it softer, then roll it out into a sausage shape, 7in (18 cm) long.

2. Ask for a saucepan of hot water. Place the chocolate in a basin over the saucepan and leave until it has melted.

3. Place the roll of marzipan on a cooling rack over a plate, to catch any drips of chocolate. Remove the basin of melted chocolate from the saucepan.

   Using a teaspoon, coat the marzipan with chocolate, then sprinkle some chocolate vermicelli over the chocolate. Leave to cool on the rack.

4. When the chocolate is hard, place the roll on a board and cut into 12 slices.

Jacqui

paper Flower-POWER!

Daisy

1

2

3

4

Everyone loves pretty flowers. And if you don't have even a window-box to your name, you can still enjoy them all the year round — thanks to "Scotties", the tissue hankies, "Fiesta" kitchen paper towel rolls, and "Andrex" toilet tissue!

Cherry Blossom

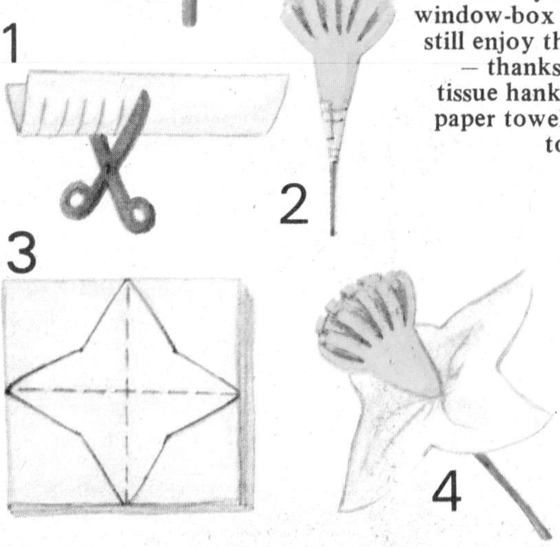

1

2

3

4

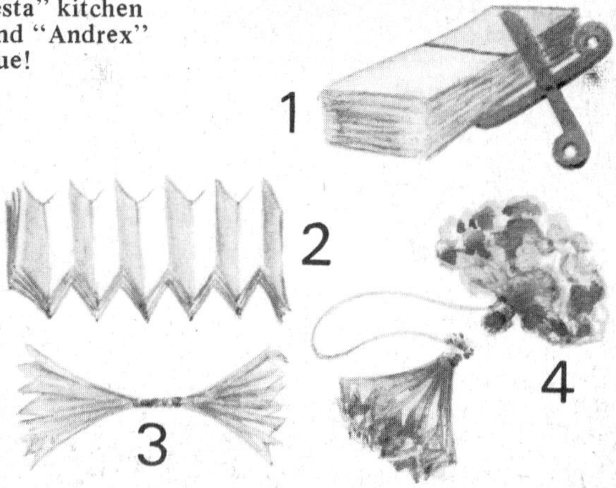

We'll start with Spring, because that's when we all look forward to seeing flowers after the winter. So, how about a bunch of daisies?

You'll need: yellow and white tissues from "Rainbow Scotties"; "Mansize Scotties"; a thin garden stick, a pipe-cleaner, and some Sellotape.

First, make the centre by folding one tissue in half lengthways, and make cuts from the folded edge towards the top, making the strips about 2½cm (1") deep and 1/3cm (1/8th") wide, as in the diagram (1). Make another piece the same, then place these two tissues together, and wind firmly around the top of your thin stick, fastening the uncut edge tightly to the stick with Sellotape.

The petals are made by putting three tissues together and cutting out a four-pointed star shape, as large as possible. By folding into quarters and making a short crease at each end, you can draw a pencil cross by joining up each crease, as shown in our sketch. Do this six times, so that you use twenty-one large tissues in all. Then push the "free" end of your stick through the centre of each star, and bring star shapes up to centre of flower, spacing out slightly to form the petal arrangement, as you wish. And, as with the flower centre, tape the centres of your star shapes firmly to the garden stick.

For smaller daisies, make the centre exactly the same, but use only one tissue fixed to a pipe-cleaner instead

of a stick. And, for the petals, fold one tissue into four and cut to a star shape, making one more star shape in this way. Then push the end of a pipe-cleaner through the centre of the two star shapes, and finish off as for the small daisy.

Cherry Blossom time comes next, using pink tissues from "Harmony Scotties" pack (four different shades of pink in one box), some fuse-wire and green thread. First, cut two 2-ply (that's two layers) of tissue into four, lengthwise, and place the strips together, so that you have the thickness of sixteen plies (or sixteen layers) Cut in half across the width (see diagram), and separate the layers, to give you 32 rectangles of single-layer tissue.

Place four single layers together and fold the length of the tissue into pleats, about 1½ cm (¾") deep, concertina style, as in the diagram. Then twist a piece of fuse-wire round the centre of the pleated tissues, and gradually separate the layers, starting with the top one and pulling up gently towards the centre, trimming if necessary, to neaten the blossom.

Make another seven blossoms in the same way, so that you can make four "pairs", by fastening one to each end of a 10 cm (4") length of thread, knotting firmly through the loop of fuse-wire, all ready to dangle from a small branch. You can just imagine how pretty a group of cherry blossom flowers would look, arranged in a vase!

paper Flower-POWER!

Rose

And, how about some Roses to see you through the summer months? They couldn't be easier to make — and all for six sheets of "Andrex" toilet tissue, some green garden wire, (or florist's wire), Sellotape, and green sticky tape or gutta-percha (florist's stem-wind). You can often pick up bargain-priced odds and ends at florists' shops, so its always worth asking.

Fold each sheet of tissue into quarters, and cut out a round, rose-shaped petal, as in the diagram, (making sure you do not cut through the bottom left-hand corner)! Then open the shape out half-way and cut in half, to give two four-ply petals. (See diagram).

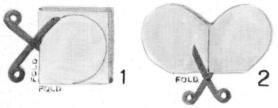

Cut a piece of green wire about 30 cm (12") long, bending one end over to a depth of about 8 cm (3¼"), and flattening as much as you can to make a stem. Next, take a petal and wind this round the thick end of the wire to cover it, repeating with another petal to look like the centre of a rose.

Make another ten petals with the other five sheets in the same way, then pinch in each one at the base for a rose-petal shape, and stick each one firmly on the wire, overlapping around the rose centre until all the petals are in place, and neatening the base with the gutta-percha or green tape.

And, to make your roses even more life-like, try "teasing-out" the tissue layers with a size 10 plastic knitting needle. For an even prettier effect, you could easily curl the edges of the tissue petals around the needle, so that, when the needle is gently drawn out, the blooms are fluffier and more natural-looking.

Leaves

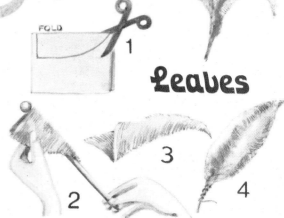

Want to make some leaves to set off your arrangement of paper roses? No problem! Just fold two sheets of green toilet tissue together, fold again, and cut the shape of the leaves you want — big and bold, delicate and ferny — it's up to you!

Slip a size 10 knitting needle into the fold, with the needle-knob towards the wider end of the leaf, and push the tissue firmly along towards the knob to crinkle the centre of the leaf, as in the diagram. Wind some fuse wire around the wider end of the leaf to give it extra shape, then you can either stick it on to a twig, arrange your leaves in bunches like little palm trees, or put them on garden canes — just as you like.

Or, if you're lucky enough to get hold of any rose prunings, (or almost any leaf sprays), at the end of the summer, you might like to preserve these to go with your tissue flowers.

All you have to do is mix ¼-pint of glycerin (which you can buy cheaply from your local chemist's shop), and ½-pint boiling water, stirring for about thirty seconds, until it is quite clear. (Ask a grown-up to help you with this, for safety's sake).

Pour into something like a kilner jar to a depth of 10 cm (4"), and plunge the stems into the liquid, leaving them for about 2 — 4 weeks. As the sprays absorb the liquid, top up each day with the remaining cold mixture. Remove the sprays when they absorb no more liquid, and tie in bundles to hang upside down in a cool place until needed. The leaves will turn to shades from greeny-bronze through to copper and deep browns, with different types of roses varying in colour — really lovely!

Just two tips before you start on your first masterpiece. Don't stand your tissue flowers on window sills — strong sunlight will soon make the flowers fade. And don't make them wilt or wrinkle by leaving them in the damp or steamy atmosphere of a kitchen or bathroom.

Otherwise, there's absolutely nothing to stop you from making enough paper flowers to fill your entire home!

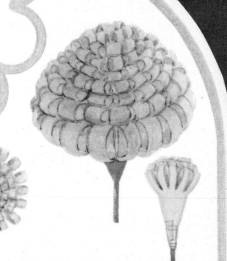

Geranium

Geraniums always give such beautifully bright splashes of colour to last us right until the Autumn — and the ones you can make from pink Scotties are no different. First, fold a tissue into half four times, and cut along the folds to make 16 little squares. (If you want pale shades, separate the tissue layers).

Fold each square into four, then diagonally, so that the centre of the square is at the bottom, and cut out the same shape petal as in the diagram, opening out flat, afterwards.

Next, cut an 8 cm (3¼'') length of fuse-wire, and either twist one end around the ends of almost-closed tweezers to form a small coil, or thread through a small bead, twisting the end of the wire to keep the bead in place. Push the free end of the wire through the centre of each set of petals, leaving the coil or the bead just clear. Pinch tissue to wire, keeping in place by doubling the wire back and coiling around the tissue, (see diagram). Open out petals.

Make remaining 15 blossoms in the same way, gathering together the fuse-wire stems, twisting into a bunch with something like garden wire, leaving a "stem" of about 20 cm (8''). Cover the stem with green sticky tape, (insulating tape from your local hardware shop will do), or gutta-percha, and open out the petals to form blossom. You could even push the wire stem into a pot of earth or garden mould, either with paper or real geranium leaves!

You can also make Hydrangeas in the same way, using pink or mauve tissues from a Harmony pack, or blue toilet tissue.

Chrysanthemum

And, to brighten a few fireside evenings, how about some Chrysanthemums? The flower centre is made in exactly the same way as that of the daisies — and the petals are made just the same, too — except that the strips should be cut 4 cm (1½'') deep and ½ cm (¼'') wide. Fasten uncut edges to a garden stick with Sellotape. Make another strip of petals and stick into place, as before, covering the clear tape around the stem of each flower with green tape.

To ring the changes, trying making the centres a different colour from the petals, or make the petals in different colours for multi-coloured flowers. With just one box of Rainbow or Harmony tissues, you could make an arrangement worthy of the Chelsea Flower Show!

Apple Blossom

Apple Blossom is also similar to make, by placing together single layers of a pink and white tissue and cutting the petals in the same way as for the geranium. Make up into single blooms, rather than clusters, using petals of one layer of white and one of pink together. Fix the blooms singly, or in little groups of three or four on to apple-tree cuttings, with leaf-buds, too, if you can get them.

Placed in water, and in a warm room, they look very attractive as the leaves come out — just like the real thing!

TUCK-IN with Tammy

What is the connection between —

AN OLD CHARM to make your sweetheart visit you?

THE QUEEN OF SHEBA?

MOUTHWATERING SMELLS from the kitchen?

In case you haven't guessed, it's

HERBS & SPICES!

*N*obody can say exactly when herbs and spices were first used, but we do know that it must have been thousands of years before the birth of Christ — because there are many stories about them in the Old Testament, such as the Queen of Sheba bringing King Solomon a gift of camels bearing spices, and Joseph (and his coat of many colours) being sold to spice-traders.

Those were the days when there were no refrigerators or deep-freezers to keep food fresh, especially in hot weather. So it's not difficult to see why herbs and spices were so important.

In the Middle Ages, European nobles had to rely on romantic voyagers, such as Drake, Raleigh, Columbus and Marco Polo to bring back herbs and spices across the seas. And, as many such travellers also told tales of doctors in faraway places such as Babylon and Abyssinia using them to treat sick people, as well as stories they'd heard of the dangers in reaching secret places where they grew, it's not surprising that quite a few herbs and spices began to seem magical, with a number of "charms" being concocted for health and good fortune. And, whether they actually worked or not, there was always that extra-delicious flavour to be added to almost any dish!

Nowadays, though, we're much luckier. Because, instead of waiting months, or even years, for any herbs and spices which take our

fancy, we can wander down to the nearest grocer's or supermarket and choose from the range of McCORMICK'S HERBS AND SPICES — just like professional cooks in the very best kitchens!

To start with, how about this delicious CHEF'S SALAD BOWL — classy enough to be served at a banquet, yet easy enough for YOU to prepare at home, with the help of McCormick's salad seasoning — a gorgeous blend of Romano Cheese, Peppers, Garlic, Poppy Seed, Celery Seed — and Sesame Seed, which early Assyrians believed their gods made into wine which they drank before the creation of Earth . . .

You will also need — 1 lettuce, 1 bunch watercress; 2 carrots; 1 cucumber (sliced); 1 onion, (sliced and separated into rings); 2 tomatoes, cut into wedges; 8 radishes, sliced; 1 avocado pear, sliced, (if you can get hold of one); McCormick ground black pepper; salt.

Wash all the vegetables, wrapping them in a clean tea-towel to soak

up the excess water, than tear the lettuce into small pieces. Peel the carrots and make "carrot curls" by peeling away thinly with a potato peeler, then put the lettuce, sprigs of watercress, carrot curls, cucumber, onion, tomatoes, radishes (and an avocado pear, if you have one) in a salad bowl. Sprinkle generously with salad seasoning, salt and black pepper.

Toss salad with a French dressing made from — ½ cup vinegar; ¾ teaspoon salt; a dash of McCormick's "MSG" Flavour Enhancer; ¼ tsp. white pepper; ½ tsp. dry mustard; 1½ cups olive or salad oil. Pour all these ingredients in a jar, cover and shake vigorously — and it's best if you can set it aside or chill for at least 30 minutes to allow all the flavours to blend, shaking again before you use it. (These ingredients make up about two cups of French dressing, so Mum could keep some in the freezer, ready for the next CHEF'S SALAD BOWL).

Enough for six to eight lucky people!

And for a "something different" T.V. snack or party dish, why not have a go at making —

Cinnamon biscuits

Half a teaspoon of Cinnamon mixed in a tumbler of hot water has always been a good remedy for colds and 'flu, long before aspirins were on sale. And did you know that Moses was told by God to use Cinnamon in preparing the holy anointing oil? Which is just one of the reasons why Cinnamon has always been a very popular ingredient in Jewish cooking.

To make about 30 rounds, you will need —

8 oz self raising flour; 1½ tsp. McCormick ground cinnamon; 5 oz butter or margarine; 4 oz castor sugar; beaten egg to mix; Bakewell baking parchment (you can buy that at most stationer's).

For the decoration; sieved icing sugar; McCormick food colourings; walnuts, chopped or halved.

Sift the flour and Cinnamon into a bowl, then rub in the butter or margarine and add the sugar. Mix to a very stiff dough with the beaten egg, and turn on to a lightly floured board. Knead gently until smooth, then put into a polythene bag and pop it into the fridge for about half an hour.

Roll out thinly, and cut into about 30 rounds (that's using a 2-inch biscuit cutter). Carefully put the rounds on to a baking sheet lined with baking parchment, and bake in a pre-heated oven, 180ºC, 350ºF, or Gas Mark 4 for 12 — 15 minutes, or until pale golden in colour. Then put the rounds on to a wire cooling rack while you're making the glace icing decoration.

Mix the sieved icing sugar with a very little water and a drop or two of food colouring, as you choose. Then, when the biscuits are cool, decorate with different coloured icing and top with chopped walnuts, or walnut halves.

Apple spice

Ingredients
1 lb (500g) cooking apples; juice ½ lemon; 6 oz (175g) margarine; 6oz (175g) soft brown sugar; 12oz (350g) wholewheat flour; 1 tsp. (5 ml) bicarbonate of soda; ¼ tsp. (1.25 ml) McCormick ground cloves; 1 tsp. (5 ml) McCormick cinnamon. ½ tsp. (2.5 ml) McCormick nutmeg; ½ tsp. (2.5 ml) McCormick ground mace; 4 oz (100g) chopped walnuts; 2 oz (50g) raisins; 6 oz (175g) chopped dates; 3 tbs. (45 ml) milk.

For the topping: 1 tablespoon (15 ml) demarara sugar; 1 oz (25g) chopped walnuts; ½ tsp. (2.5 ml) McCormick cinnamon.

Set the oven at 170ºC, 325ºF, Gas Mark 3. Peel, quarter and slice the apples, then place them in a pan with 4 tablespoons (60 ml) water and the lemon juice. Cover and cook gently until soft, then mash with a wooden spoon and leave to cool.

Next, cream the margarine and sugar until pale and fluffy. Mix the flour with the bicarbonate of soda and spices, then stir into the creamed mixture with the walnuts, raisins, dates and milk. Turn the mixture into a greased 2lb (2 kg) loaf tin, then mix the topping ingredients and sprinkle over the cake. Bake for 1¼ — 1½ hours. Leave in the tin for 15 minutes, then turn out on to a wire rack to cool.

ALL THE FUN OF THE FAIR

Once upon a time, pleasure wasn't something which the ordinary person could enjoy very often. Life was harder than anyone today can possibly imagine, with very long working hours — and, as even Christmas was always a solemn occasion, with no present-giving or special food, the only treats anyone could be really sure of having, were the fairs which took place once or twice a year.

These fairs were usually no more than a meeting for buying and selling between all the farming folk who came along. Almost everyone lived by the land in those days, which is why many of the fairs were planned at the end of a farming season, when people went to Church to pay their "tithes" or taxes to the Crown — like Lady-Day, Candlemas and Michaelmas Fairs. This was also the time when young people went along to stand at a special place, hoping to be offered a job, to be "hired", and many of the fairs were known as "Hiring Fairs".

Sometimes, there might have been a travelling minstrel or a puppet show to liven things up. But it was quite a long time before people thought of having anything like swings or roundabouts to keep the children happy — just a wooden seat on ropes, and a cart-wheel mounted on a wooden post or spindle, with the children sitting in the spokes, pulled round by a plodding cart-horse tethered to the rim!

Then, with the invention of the steam engine, things really began to perk up. Thanks to the steam railways, people were able to travel much further than they ever had before, which meant that each fair could attract customers from far and wide, especially with new and better attractions to keep visitors happy.

One of the first "new arrivals" on the scene was the **bioscope**, which came from France and Italy — a beautifully-framed screen on which pictures were shown, one after the

other at quite a speed, to create the illusion of moving pictures, rather like "flicker-books" which we can still buy today.

Steam-driven organs playing gay music also did a great deal to attract the crowds to "side-shows", like boxing booths, animal collections and coconut shies.

And, as the bioscopes and organs became more widespread, the more elaborate the decoration on them became, often with fierce competition between the showmen to see who could provide the best attraction, and the best-decorated living wagons and caravans for people to admire and make note of, as they travelled the road from one fair to another.

One of the men who made a living out of carving the beautiful decorations for showmen's wagons and fairground equipment was Frederick Savage, from King's Lynn, in Norfolk. And it was his firm which, in 1870, marketed the first steam-driven roundabout,

The steam-driven yacht "Neptune" was built around 1911 at Brownroyd, Bradford, and was originally hand-operated by two men, with a rope at each end.

complete with the instantly popular "gallopers" — horses or birds which rose up and down in time to the much-loved organ music. Every possible part was painted or carved with patterns, flowers, butterflies and birds, gleaming in the light from the magnificent " barley sugar" twisted brass struts and hand-rails. No wonder that the showman always had his name specially painted around the top rim, for everyone to see!

Steam-driven roundabouts are extremely rare these days, but you can still see and enjoy a ride on an original Savage's roundabout, complete with the magnificent organ and steam puffing gently from the little funnel at the top, at **Bressingham Gardens and Steam Museum**, near Diss, in Norfolk — not so far from the place where Savage had his firm. (You can visit Bressingham either on Sundays or Thursdays from June until the beginning of September, and on Sundays during May and late September).

The steam-driven roundabout proved so popular that Savages soon began developing other fair-ground attractions — such as the Venetian Gondola Switchback Ride. Only one of these Switchbacks still remain, but you can admire its ornate decoration carved from solid wood and the inset cut-glass panels at The Thursford Collection, near Fakenham, also in Norfolk, which is open every day from Easter weekend to 31st October, and every Sunday and Bank Holiday throughout the year, from 2.00 pm — 5.30 pm.

By this time, fairgrounds were really big business, with many attractions having wonderful names. One was the **Razzle Dazzle**, where people paid to enjoy being swung around sharply in open carriages — a ride which was to spark off many of the more modern fairground attractions which we know today.

Then there was **The Cakewalk**, a sort of wooden hump-backed bridge in sections which lurched and wobbled whilst people tried to get from one side to the other, hauling themselves along by the handrail, and **Chair-O-Planes** — still very popular, but driven by electricity now, and not steam.

With all these different attractions to choose from, and the more wide-spread use of electricity, people gradually began demanding more breath-taking rides and spectacular attractions. The old days of the "Hiring Fairs" had long since passed!

Photographs by Richard Searight.

The biggest problem then was dismantling and transporting all the equipment from one place to another. So the idea of permanent **Pleasure Parks** must have been a very welcome inspiration!

They soon became firmly established in the U.S.A. after the opening of the world famous Disneyland, with Europe — especially Holland and West Germany — following suit.

And now, Great Britain can boast its very own Pleasure Park Complex, rated among the top ten in the whole world — **Alton Towers**, situated between Leek and Ashbourne, in North Staffordshire.

Further attractions to be found at Alton Towers include the Chinese Pagoda (top) and the Rock Gardens.

Alton Towers is actually the name of the site's ruined mansion, once the home of the Earls of Shrewsbury, and where visitors can explore the ancient cellars and see the beautiful views from the battlements.

But, what most people come to see now are the really spectacular attractions — over thirty in all — such as the breath-taking **Cable Car Rides**, a space-age **Cine 2000** cinema presentation, showing exciting car chases, big dipper rides and views from the Grand Canyon in such a way that viewers feel they're actually taking part. Then there's Europe's biggest **Around the World in 80 days** ride, Britain's only all-weather bobsleigh run, a swinging **Pirate Galleon,** and — perhaps the most spectacular and most famous — the biggest **Corkscrew** Roller Coaster in the world, where riders can enjoy the thrilling sensation of hanging upside down in mid-air, as the carriages whizz around the three loops of the **Corkscrew** frame-work — hair-raising! Especially when you remember that the **Corkscrew** cost two and a half million pounds — a price which could not even have been imagined by those old showmen, travelling in their living wagons.

But even the **Corkscrew** might seem cheap at the price, compared with the very latest attraction at **Alton Towers** — the **Canadian Log Flume**, where you rush down foaming cataracts of wild water. It's the World's biggest, built and installed at a cost of no less than five million pounds! So, it seems that people are **still** demanding bigger and better attractions!

And, although **Alton Towers** intends looking towards the future, with many new leisure attractions planned for the coming years, so work will continue to restore the mansion to its former glory, as one of Britain's biggest stately homes. Its lovely grounds and some of the most stunning and beautiful gardens in all Europe providing the perfect setting for fun and laughter.

So perhaps the link between steam roundabouts and fairground organs, and the **Corkscrew** and **Canadian Log Flume** is much closer than most people imagine.

After all, as every showman, wood-carver, steam-organ maker, and Pleasure Park owner would agree, it's still the same business — about making people happy. And that never changes, whatever age we're living in!

CONTINUED FROM PAGE 72

Later...

I'VE JUST BEEN TO THE HOSPITAL. THE MAGISTRATE'S RECOVERED BUT HE'S COMPLETELY LOST HIS MEMORY... DOESN'T KNOW WHERE HE'S BEEN.

I SEE! WILL YOU LEAVE US NOW, JULIE. I WANT TO SPEAK TO THE DOCTOR ALONE.

THE DOCTOR WAS MENTIONED IN THAT NOTE AS WELL. FATHER MUST WANT TO SPEAK TO HIM ABOUT IT. I WISH I KNEW WHAT IT ALL MEANT.

CRIKEY, THEY'VE BEEN TALKING A LONG TIME. IT'S NEARLY DARK NOW.

JULIE!

DOCTOR!

SSSH! I DON'T WANT YOUR FATHER TO HEAR. I'VE SOMETHING IMPORTANT TO TELL YOU, JULIE.

LISTEN CAREFULLY, JULIE. YOUR FATHER PLANS TO DESTROY THAT FAIRGROUND. HE'S A HARD MAN AND WILL STOP AT NOTHING.

BECAUSE OF THAT NOTE... WHAT DID IT MEAN ABOUT SETTLING A SCORE?

IT'S FROM AN OLD ENEMY OF YOUR FATHER'S, JULIE. THERE'S NOTHING I CAN DO, BUT IF ANYTHING HAPPENS TO ME YOU MUST UNLOCK THE TOP DRAWER ON MY DESK WITH THIS KEY. THERE'S A FILE THERE... GIVE IT TO THE NEWSPAPERS. WILL YOU DO THAT?

DON'T FORGET, JULIE. THE WHOLE LIFE OF THE VILLAGE COULD DEPEND ON YOU!

I-I FEEL SCARED! SOMETHING TERRIBLE'S GOING TO HAPPEN IN BAYCHURCH AND I KNOW I WON'T BE ABLE TO STOP IT. I KNOW IT!

NOW, TAKE THE KEY, JULIE, I MUST BE GOING!

C – CAN'T YOU TELL ME ANYMORE, DOCTOR?

I – I'M SCARED. SOMETHING TERRIBLE IS GOING TO HAPPEN. BUT WHAT?

JULIE, COME IN!

FROM NOW ON, YOU MUST GO NOWHERE NEAR THE FAIRGROUND. IN FACT I FORBID YOU TO STRAY FROM THE HOUSE TILL IT LEAVES TOWN!

WHY, FATHER?

BECAUSE THAT CLOWN WILL STOP AT NOTHING TO DESTROY THE GOOD NAME OF WHITLAND. NOW DO AS I SAY AND GO TO BED – IT'S GETTING LATE!

YES, FATHER.

THE HOUSE OF MEMORIES SAID I MUST SOLVE THE FAIRGROUND'S MYSTERY TO FIND OUT WHO MY REAL PARENTS WERE. BUT I KNOW NOTHING EXCEPT THERE'S SOME KIND OF FEUD BETWEEN MY FATHER AND THE CLOWN. WHAT DOES IT ALL MEAN?

Next morning...

WHAT'S THIS – A PETITION? FATHER IS TRYING TO GET THE FAIRGROUND RUN OUT OF TOWN!

BAN THIS FAIRGROUND

Just then...

AGH – WHAT'S HAPPENING?

IT'S PEOPLE FROM THE VILLAGE. W – WHY ARE THEY THROWING STONES AT US?

THAT'S WHAT WE THINK OF YOUR PETITION, SIR EDGAR!

YOU MAY OWN MOST OF THIS VILLAGE BUT YOU DON'T OWN US. WE LIKE THE FAIRGROUND!

SO THERE'S NO NEED FOR A RIOT! YOU DON'T HAVE TO SIGN THE PETITION, DO YOU?

98

NO, JACKSON! YOU'LL GET HURT.

DON'T YOU WORRY, SIR EDGAR. I'LL SHOW EM . . . TRAMPING ALL OVER MY BEGONIAS LIKE THAT.

TAKE THAT!

HE'S A **NUTTER** – RUN FOR IT!

The gardener had struck out harder than he meant . . .

LOOK! HE'S BEGINNING TO COME ROUND.

PERHAPS NOW WE'LL GET SOME EXPLANATION OF THE VILLAGERS' BEHAVIOUR!

I'M SORRY IF WE'VE DONE ANYTHING WRONG. I DON'T KNOW WHAT CAME OVER US. WE WERE AT THE FAIR AND THIS GUY STARTED RANTING ON ABOUT YOUR PETITION AND ABOUT HOW WE SHOULDN'T STAND FOR IT – HE WAS DRESSED LIKE A CLOWN. I DON'T REMEMBER AFTER THAT!

I MIGHT HAVE KNOWN!

SO HE THINKS HE CAN USE THE VILLAGERS AGAINST ME NOW. WELL, I'LL SHOW HIM!

CONCRETE AND BARBED WIRE – FATHER'S MAKING THIS HOUSE MORE LIKE A PRISON THAN EVER. I CAN'T STAND IT ! I'VE **GOT** TO GET OUT FOR JUST A LITTLE WHILE.

OH, IT'S GOOD TO FEEL FREE! FUNNY, THE FAIRGROUND LOOKS SO HARMLESS FROM HERE.

JULIE, IS THAT YOU? I MUST SPEAK TO YOU!

IT'S MR. FRASER, THE FAIRGROUND OWNER. I'D BETTER GET OUT OF HERE . . .

DON'T RUN AWAY, JULIE. IT'S ABOUT CARLA.

CARLA! HAS ANYTHING HAPPENED TO HER?

SHE'S ILL, JULIE . . . **VERY** ILL. SHE CAN'T BE MOVED AND THE DOCTOR REFUSES TO VISIT HER. PLEASE WILL **YOU** GO AND TALK TO HIM?

HE LOOKS SO WORRIED BUT IT COULD BE A **TRICK**.

I DON'T BELIEVE YOU! LET ME SEE HER.

POOR CARLA! OKAY, MR. FRASER. I'LL GO AND HAVE A WORD WITH THE DOCTOR.

Julie ran all the way to the surgery. . .

PLEASE, DOCTOR, YOU MUST COME. SHE'S **REALLY** ILL.

I THOUGHT THIS WAS ONE OF THE CLOWN'S SCHEMES TO GET ME IN HIS CLUTCHES BUT IF YOU SAY IT'S TRUE, THEN I'LL COME.

IF THE CLOWN IS MY FATHER'S ENEMY, WHY DOES HE WANT YOU, DOCTOR?

BECAUSE LONG AGO I DID SOMETHING TO HIM FOR YOUR FATHER, JULIE. SOMETHING THAT HAS **MADE** HIM WHAT HE IS TODAY.

SHE'S HAD A BAD BOUT OF FOOD POISONING, BUT SHE'LL BE ALL RIGHT — THIS'LL SOON HAVE HER FIT AGAIN. I'LL WALK YOU HOME, JULIE!

NO, JULIE, PLEASE STAY!

DON'T BE LONG, JULIE. REMEMBER THIS PLACE ISN'T SAFE FOR YOU.

I'VE NOTHING TO FEAR FROM CARLA.

TH — THANK YOU FOR COMING, DOCTOR.

I HEARD IT WAS YOU WHO BROUGHT THE DOCTOR . . . THANK YOU! CAN WE BE FRIENDS AGAIN?

OH, YES, CARLA, I'D LIKE THAT VERY MUCH!

I FOUND OUT, TOO. YOU WERE RIGHT ABOUT THE CLOWN, JULIE. HE **DOES** HAVE SOME SORT OF EVIL INFLUENCE OVER MY FATHER. WHO IS HE, JULIE? I NEVER SEE HIM WITHOUT HIS MAKE-UP.

ALL I KNOW IS HE'S AN ENEMY OF MY FATHER AND THE DOCTOR — AND EVERYONE IN THE VILLAGE. HE JUST USES EVERYBODY!

I WON'T FEEL SAFE TILL I'M OUT OF THIS FAIRGROUND — THERE'S AN UNEASY ATMOSPHERE HERE — AS THOUGH I'M BEING **WATCHED**!

THAT'S ODD! I COULD HAVE SWORN THIS WAS THE WAY OUT BUT IT'S A DEAD END!

HA, HA, HA!

I'VE GOT TO REACH THE DOOR, BEFORE THIS PLACE DRIVES ME CRAZY.

Later, as Julie walked past the crazy house...

I HOPE THE DOCTOR GOT HOME SAFELY. HELLO, WONDER WHAT'S HAPPENING OVER THERE?

POOR MAN, SEEMS HE FELL RIGHT FROM THAT DOORWAY UP THERE! IT'S NOT SUPPOSED TO OPEN — HE MUST'VE FORCED IT!

IT'S DOCTOR PEARSON!

HE'S GIVEN HIMSELF A RIGHT CRACK ON THE HEAD. WE'D BETTER GET HIM TO HOSPITAL.

THE CLOWN MUST HAVE GOT TO THE DOCTOR! IT'S ALL MY FAULT FOR HAVING BROUGHT DOCTOR PEARSON TO THE FAIRGROUND IN THE FIRST PLACE! HE KNEW SOMETHING WOULD HAPPEN TO HIM!

IF ANYTHING HAPPENS TO ME, JULIE, YOU MUST LOOK FOR THE FILE IN MY DESK.

I'VE STILL GOT THE KEY. I MUST GO TO THE DOCTOR'S HOUSE RIGHT AWAY!

Soon, in the doctor's study...

THIS IS THE FILE THE DOCTOR TOLD ME ABOUT. THE NAME ON IT IS ALAN BARKER. TH-THAT'S THE CLOWN'S NAME!

THESE OLD NEWSPAPER CLIPPINGS ARE ABOUT THE CLOWN...

"ALAN BARKER, SCIENTIST, WAS TODAY JAILED FOR THREE YEARS FOR THE MANSLAUGHTER OF EMILY CARSON. BARKER HAD ATTEMPTED TO CURE THE GIRL BY MEANS OF A MACHINE HE HAD INVENTED... BUT EMILY WORSENED AND DIED. GIVING EVIDENCE, DOCTOR PEARSON SAID THAT EMILY WAS SUFFERING FROM A QUITE CURABLE DISEASE, IF BARKER HAD NOT INTERFERED..."

HERE'S EMILY CARSON'S MEDICAL RECORD, WRITTEN BY DOCTOR PEARSON.

MEDICAL RECORD

I-IF THIS RECORD'S **TRUE** THE DOCTOR DELIBERATELY LIED IN COURT. NO WONDER THE CLOWN HATES HIM. THE DOCTOR HAD HIM JAILED FOR SOMETHING HE DIDN'T DO. BUT WHY?

BECAUSE I ASKED HIM TO!

FATHER! WHAT ARE YOU DOING HERE?

THE SAME AS YOU, JULIE . . . I CAME FOR THE FILE AS SOON AS I HEARD OF THE DOCTOR'S ACCIDENT.

WHY DID YOU WANT TO DESTROY BARKER, FATHER? WHAT HAD HE EVER DONE TO YOU?

LOOK AT THIS PHOTO, JULIE.

IT'S A PHOTO OF YOUR DAUGHTER . . . THE ONE WHO DIED BEFORE I WAS ADOPTED. IT'S HER WEDDING PICTURE.

YOU DON'T RECOGNISE THE GROOM, OF COURSE. YOU'VE NEVER SEEN THE CLOWN WITHOUT HIS MAKE-UP . . . **NO ONE** HAS. BUT THEY'RE BOTH **BARKER!**

AGAINST ALL MY WISHES, THAT QUACK SCIENTIST BECAME MY SON-IN-LAW. I COULDN'T STAND TO HAVE THAT **NOBODY** PART OF THE GREAT WHITLAND FAMILY.

SO FOR THAT YOU DESTROYED HIS LIFE AND HIS CAREER. THAT'S **TERRIBLE!** I CAN **UNDERSTAND** WHY HE CAME BACK FOR REVENGE NOW!

BUT IF WE GIVE THIS FILE TO BE PUBLISHED IN THE NEWSPAPERS, HIS NAME WILL BE CLEARED AND HE'LL BE SATISFIED.

AND DESTROY **OUR** NAME? **NEVER!** HE HAS A TALENT AS A THIRD-RATE MAGICIAN BUT HE DOESN'T FRIGHTEN ME WITH HIS TRICKS . . .

THERE! THAT'S AN END TO THE MATTER!

HE'S DESTROYING THE ONE THING THAT WOULD APPEASE THE CLOWN. THE DOCTOR SAID THE WHOLE OF THE VILLAGE DEPENDED ON THAT BEING PUBLISHED.

OH, LOOK, FATHER! LOOK AT THE FLAMES! THE CLOWN KNOWS WHAT'S HAPPENING. HE'LL STOP AT NOTHING NOW – TO GET REVENGE. OH, WHAT HAVE YOU **DONE?**

FATHER, FATHER — **PLEASE** LOOK!

THERE'S NOTHING THERE! IT'S JUST YOUR IMAGINATION — YOU ALWAYS WERE A FANCIFUL CHILD!

PERHAPS FATHER'S RIGHT. I LET MY IMAGINATION RUN AWAY WITH ME... BUT THERE'S DANGER COMING. I CAN FEEL IT.

Later, at home . . .

YOU WILL GO TO YOUR ROOM, JULIE, AND STAY THERE!

FATHER'S RUTHLESS, AND SO SURE OF HIS OWN STRENGTH AGAINST THE CLOWN'S.

BUT I KNOW THE CLOWN'S POWERS. I'VE GOT TO TRY AND PERSUADE HIM NOT TO DO ANYTHING TO THE VILLAGE. I JUST HOPE THIS VINE WILL HOLD MY WEIGHT.

M-MUSTN'T LOOK DOWN...OR I'LL GET DIZZY...

PHEW! MADE IT! NOW TO FIND THE CLOWN.

THE FAIRGROUND — IT'S-IT'S IN DARKNESS. LOOKS LIKE EVERYONE'S GONE TO BED.

THAT'S THE CLOWN'S CARAVAN, AND THERE'S A LIGHT ON — HE MUST STILL BE UP. OH, I WISH I DIDN'T FEEL SO SCARED.

DO NOT DISTURB

WHO'S THAT? CAN'T YOU SEE THE NOTICE...GET OUT!

GOSH! THIS IS THE FIRST TIME I'VE SEEN HIM WITHOUT HIS MAKE-UP... HE DOESN'T LOOK FRIGHTENING AT ALL NOW.

PLEASE LISTEN TO ME, MR. BARKER. I KNOW WHAT MY FATHER DID TO YOU AND HE WAS WRONG TO SEND YOU TO JAIL FOR SOMETHING YOU DIDN'T DO. BUT IT ALL HAPPENED SO LONG AGO...

SO YOU'VE COME TO TELL ME TO FORGIVE AND FORGET? WELL, TIME WILL NEVER HEAL MY WOUNDS...

I WAS A BRILLIANT SCIENTIST, BUT I WASN'T GOOD ENOUGH TO MARRY HIS DAUGHTER – SO HE FRAMED ME. AND SHE DIED THINKING I WAS A CRIMINAL.

AND-AND OUR BABY DIED, TOO – BEFORE I HAD A CHANCE TO SEE HER. ALL I'VE GOT LEFT IN MY HEART IS VENGEANCE!

BUT THE VILLAGERS HAVE DONE NOTHING TO YOU.

THAT'S SIR EDGAR'S CONCERN. HE CAN STOP THIS ANYTIME HE WANTS BY CLEARING MY NAME. NOW GO!

FATHER WILL NEVER DO THAT.

I-I'VE FAILED.

JULIE, IS THAT YOU?

DO NOT DISTURB

OH, CARLA, WHAT'S GOING TO HAPPEN? CAN'T YOUR FATHER STOP THIS? HE OWNS THE FAIRGROUND.

IN NAME ONLY, JULIE. MY FATHER GOT BADLY IN DEBT AND THE CLOWN BOUGHT ALL THE BILLS. HE COULD TAKE OVER THE FAIRGROUND ANYTIME HE WANTS. WE'RE HELPLESS.

BUT I KNOW THE CLOWN'S WORKING ON ANOTHER OF HIS DEVILISH MACHINES. HE'S GOT SOMETHING NASTY PLANNED FOR THE VILLAGERS. IF I CAN FIND IT I'LL DESTROY IT.

BE CAREFUL, CARLA.

DON'T WORRY – I WILL.

I MUST GET HOME NOW BEFORE I'M MISSED. GOOD LUCK!

Next day...

I'M GOING TO COURT TODAY, JULIE. THEY'RE TRYING MISS GREY'S CASE.

MISS GREY! I'D ALMOST FORGOTTEN SHE'D BEEN ARRESTED FOR PICKPOCKETING. I'D LIKE TO GO WITH YOU.

MY POOR SISTER. THEY MUST FIND HER INNOCENT. SHE DIDN'T KNOW WHAT SHE WAS DOING.

THE CLOWN MADE HER DO IT BECAUSE SHE KNEW ABOUT HIS FRAME-UP. THAT WAS HIS REVENGE ON HER.

105

YOUR HONOUR, THE ACCUSED, MISS GREY, WAS ARRESTED AT THE FAIRGROUND IN POSSESSION OF ARTICLES NOT BELONGING TO HER...

AND I WILL PROVE... I WILL PROVE...

WHAT'S WRONG WITH HIM? HE LOOKS AS THOUGH HE'S GOING TO FAINT.

HUH! WHY SHOULD I PROVE ANYTHING! I DON'T FEEL LIKE WORKING TODAY!

EH? WH-WHAT'S HAPPENING?

HA, HA! YOU'RE QUITE RIGHT! THIS IS A LOT OF BORING OLD RUBBISH. CASE IS DISMISSED!

ISN'T IT WONDERFUL! I'M CLEARED. NOTHING'S HAPPENED TO ME!

BUT SOMETHING STRANGE IS HAPPENING IN THIS COURT.

I KNOW! LET'S PLAY LEAP-FROG INSTEAD!

GREAT IDEA!

WHEEE! OVER I GO!

I WANT TO PLAY!

ME, TOO!

ALL THE MEN SEEM TO BE ACTING LIKE SCHOOLBOYS EXCEPT FOR OLD MR. GREGSON AND FATHER. THIS MUST BE THE CLOWN'S DOING. WHAT'S HE UP TO?

IT'S INCREDIBLE! I'VE NEVER SEEN ANYTHING LIKE IT!

THEY'VE BEEN AFFECTED AS WELL!

OI! GET BACK HERE AND DRIVE THE BUS. I'VE GOT SHOPPING TO DO!

DRIVE IT YOURSELF! I'D RATHER PLAY FOOTBALL!

Soon, back home . . .

OH, SIR, DINNER ISN'T READY! I DON'T KNOW WHAT TO DO. THE COOK'S BEEN READING COMICS ALL MORNING.

I'LL PHONE THE POLICE. THEY'LL SOON PUT A STOP TO THIS!

YOU SHOULD PUT A STOP TO IT! IF IT WASN'T FOR YOU THE CLOWN WOULDN'T BE DOING THIS TO THE VILLAGERS!

HELLO! LET ME SPEAK TO THE CHIEF SUPERINTENDANT!

I'M SORRY, SIR. I'M AFRAID THE SUPERINTENDENT IS . . . ER . . . WELL . . . HE'S PLAYING COPS AND ROBBERS DOWN IN THE PARK AT THIS MOMENT IN TIME.

THEN GET ME AN OUTSIDE LINE TO THE NEXT TOWN'S POLICE STATION. THEY CAN'T BE AFFECTED.

I'M SORRY, SIR, ONLY LOCAL LINES ARE OPEN. THE OUTSIDE LINES AREN'T WORKING. THE ENGINEERS ARE PLAYING COWBOYS AND INDIANS — THEY'VE CUT THE WIRES!

WHY DON'T YOU JUST TELL THE TRUTH ABOUT HOW YOU FRAMED BARKER ALL THOSE YEARS AGO? THAT'S ALL HE WANTS. IT'LL BE ALL OVER THEN!

BARKER WON'T BEAT ME. I'LL DRIVE TO THE NEXT VILLAGE AND GET HELP!

HE'S NOT EVEN LISTENING TO ME. I THINK I'LL GO TO THE FAIRGROUND AND TAKE A LOOK AROUND. PERHAPS I CAN DO SOMETHING.

THE VILLAGE FEELS EERIE. NO ONE'S AROUND EXCEPT WOMEN AND SOME OLDER MEN LIKE MY FATHER WHO DON'T SEEM TO BE AFFECTED. WHY?

WHERE HAVE ALL THE MEN GONE?

TO THE FAIR, NO DOUBT. MY HUSBAND MADE OFF THERE WITH ALL MY HOUSEKEEPING. I — I DON'T KNOW WHAT'S HAPPENING TO HIM — TO ANY OF THEM!

THAT WOMAN WAS RIGHT. THEY'RE ALL HERE. HEY — THERE'S CARLA AND HER FATHER. I MUST SPEAK TO THEM.

CARLA, WHAT'S HAPPENING?

IT'S ONE OF THE CLOWN'S MACHINES, JULIE. IT'S MAKING ALL THE MEN OF WORKING AGE ACT LIKE KIDS. THEY'RE SPENDING ALL THEIR MONEY AT THE FAIR.

AND IF WE CLOSE DOWN THE CLOWN MAY DO SOMETHING WORSE. WE DON'T EVEN KNOW WHERE THE MACHINE IS. IT'S HOPELESS. WHAT CAN I DO?

Meanwhile . . .

THIS STUPID CAR'S STALLED BUT I'LL WALK TO THE NEXT VILLAGE. THAT CLOWN CAN'T BEAT A WHITLAND!

BAYCHURCH 2   HEATHWELL 3½

WHAT THE . . ! THERE'S SOMETHING STOPPING ME GOING ANY FURTHER . . . LIKE AN INVISIBLE WALL!

Much later . . .

THE CLOWN'S CUT THE VILLAGE OFF FROM THE OUTSIDE WORLD.

NOW DO YOU BELIEVE HOW POWERFUL HE IS? YOU MUST TELL THE VILLAGERS HOW YOU FRAMED HIM AND CLEAR HIS NAME. THE VILLAGE IS IN CHAOS! ONLY YOU CAN SAVE IT NOW.

NO — NEVER! IT WOULD MEAN DESTROYING MY OWN GOOD NAME. THE WHITLANDS HAVE BEEN RESPECTED IN BAYCHURCH FOR CENTURIES!

OH, LOOK . . . THE LIGHTS ARE BEGINNING TO DIM!

THE ELECTRICITY SUPPLY MUST HAVE FAILED BECAUSE NONE OF THE MEN HAVE BEEN DOING REPAIRS.

BUT THE FAIRGROUND LIGHTS ARE STILL WORKING. THEY HAVE THEIR OWN GENERATOR.

WHEN BARKER, THE CLOWN, WAS IMPRISONED, HIS WIFE AND THEIR BABY DAUGHTER CAME BACK TO LIVE WITH HER FATHER SIR EDGAR. BUT ONE STORMY NIGHT THEY HAD A QUARREL ABOUT BARKER AND SHE LEFT IN THE CAR.

IT IS, JULIE. IT'S TIME YOU HEARD THE WHOLE TRUTH.

At that time there was a large cypress tree in the drive. It was struck by lightning and toppled just as she passed. . .

She was killed immediately. Sir Edgar clung to his baby grand-daughter in his grief. . .

THIS CHILD IS PART WHITLAND — SHE BELONGS WITH ME! BARKER MUST NEVER CLAIM HER!

IT TOOK VERY LITTLE EFFORT ON MY PART TO FORGE ANOTHER DEATH CERTIFICATE FOR THE CHILD AS WELL. THEN SIR WHITLAND ADOPTED HER. THAT CHILD WAS YOU, JULIE!

MY HEAD'S SPINNING. YOU-YOU MEAN SIR EDGAR'S REALLY MY GRANDFATHER?

I-I MUST HAVE TIME TO THINK. . .ON MY OWN!

JULIE, COME BACK! DON'T DO ANYTHING FOOLISH.

Meanwhile, Sir Edgar had made his way to the fair . . .

ARE YOU LOOKING FOR ME, SIR EDGAR?

YES, BARKER. BUT WHAT HAVE YOU DONE TO THE VILLAGERS NOW? THEY'RE FROZEN LIKE STATUES.

A SIMPLE HYPNOTIC TRICK. BUT THEY ARE STATUES WHO CAN STILL HEAR AND SEE, SIR EDGAR. THEY ARE MY WITNESSES FOR WHEN YOU CLEAR MY NAME!

NEVER! I ONLY CAME TO TELL YOU THAT NOTHING YOU COULD EVER DO WOULD MAKE ME CONFESS!

110

At that moment . . .

THERE'S NO USE THINKING ABOUT IT ON MY OWN. I'VE GOT TO SEE THE CLOWN — MY REAL FATHER!

Julie hardly noticed the frozen villagers. She only had eyes for one . . .

THERE HE IS — STANDING ON THE MERRY-GO-ROUND.

JULIE! WHAT ARE YOU DOING HERE? COME BACK!

SOON MY FATHER WILL KNOW WHO I AM — THEN HE'LL LEAVE THE VILLAGE ALONE.

YOU SAY THERE'S NOTHING WILL MAKE YOU CONFESS, SIR EDGAR. WELL, WE'LL SEE.

WHAT THE . .? THE MERRY-GO-ROUND'S STARTING.

THE MERRY-GO-ROUND WILL GO FASTER AND FASTER TILL YOU OWN UP, SIR EDGAR. AND WITH EVERY TURN YOUR DAUGHTER'S LIFE WILL BE MORE IN DANGER!

N-NO — WAIT! YOU'VE GOT TO LISTEN TO ME!

TOO LATE. . . IT'S GOING SO FAST. . .FEEL DIZZY. . .SICK. . .

I-I CAN'T DESTROY THE NAME OF WHITLAND. I'VE NOTHING TO SAY!

HE'D LET HIS OWN DAUGHTER DIE TO SAVE HIS PRECIOUS PRIDE — AND THE NAME OF WHITLAND! BUT I CAN'T BE RESPONSIBLE FOR MURDER. I MUST STOP THE MACHINE.

OH NO! THE LEVER'S JAMMED!

D-DON'T WORRY, GIRL — I'LL GET YOU OFF.

WRAP YOUR ARMS TIGHTLY ROUND MY NECK AND HOLD ON! WE'RE GOING TO JUMP FOR IT!

THE END

I'M OFF TO EVENING CLASSES, SIS. THEN THE TOWN WON'T BE ABLE TO CALL CANDIDATE BROWN, AN IGNORAMUS!

SEE YOU LATER!

HE'S SET HIS HEART ON BEING THE TOWN'S M.P., I HOPE HE MAKES IT!

And at long last . . .

VOTE FOR JOE BROWN

VOTE FOR FRED PROUDFOOT!

OUR GRANDAD WOULD HAVE BEEN SO PROUD, HELEN!

THERE'S THE RIVAL CANDIDATE — BUT HE'S AN OUTSIDER, FROM DOWN SOUTH — SO YOUR JOE SHOULD PULL IN THE VOTES!

But, next day . . .

HECK — A POSH VELVET SOFA! WHOEVER'S GOT THE EMPTY COTTAGE TWO DOORS DOWN FROM US, MUST BE LOADED!

HE IS — BUT FRED PROUDFOOT'S GOING TO SLUM IT LIKE ONE OF US IN A SUB-STANDARD DUMP!

THAT'S RIGHT! I'M GOING TO LIVE AMONGST MY FUTURE CONSTITUENTS — MAKE THEM FEEL I'M ONE OF THEM, AND ALL THAT JAZZ!

I SEE!

AND I SEE WHAT YOUR GAME IS, MR BIG-MAN FROM DOWN SOUTH. WAIT TILL I TELL JOE!

IT'S NOT FAIR! YOU'RE THE ONE WHO KNOWS THE LOCALS' PROBLEMS! AND HE'LL NEVER BE ONE OF US, WITH HIS PLUSH SOFA AND —

COOL IT, SIS. LET THE TOWNSFOLK DECIDE FOR THEMSELVES. THEY'RE NOT FOOLS!

And sure enough . . .

LOOK AT THAT, LASS — HE'S GOT JOINERS AND PLUMBERS PUTTING HIS COTTAGE TO RIGHTS —

. . . WHILE THE REST OF THE HOUSES IN THE ROW, CAN GO HANG! THAT'S HOW MUCH MR. PROUDFOOT CARES!

JOE'S RIGHT. THE FOLK ARE WEIGHING HIM UP!

Then, at school . . .

THERE'S GLORIA PROUDFOOT, DISHING OUT PRESENTS TO THE OTHER GIRLS — I WONDER WHY?

THANKS, GLORIA!

ENJOY YOUR PRESENTS — AND I'M SURE YOU'LL COAX YOUR DADS TO VOTE FOR MY DAD!

SO THAT'S HER GAME — BRIBERY!

DON'T WORRY, SHARON. SHE CAN'T BUY US, OR OUR DADS! MY DAD'S VOTING FOR YOUR JOE!

EVERYTHING'S FINE, JOE. FOLK ARE SEEING THROUGH THE PLASTIC PROUDFOOTS!

I KNEW THEY WOULD! LET ME PIN THIS ON — YOU'RE MY ELECTION AGENT NUMBER ONE, SIS!

THESE HOUSES ARE LONG OVER-DUE FOR DEMOLITION! IF JOE MAKES IT TO PARLIAMENT, HE'LL PUT THINGS TO RIGHT IN LEECHESTER, I KNOW IT!

VOTE FOR JOE BROWN

JOE'S DOING IT FOR YOU TOO, GRANDAD. YOU'D BE A PROUD OLD MAN TODAY, IF YOU WERE ALIVE!

Some days later . . .

IT'S A FINE AFTERNOON, GIRLS — SO WE'LL HAVE A LIVE HISTORY LESSON — OUTDOORS!

GOODY. I WONDER WHERE MISS BRETT WILL TAKE US?

WE'LL TOUR THE TOWN'S OLD CEMETERY — IT'S FULL OF INTEREST.

HECK — THE GRAVES ARE ANCIENT, MISS. LOOK AT THAT ONE — HAL BUTTERSWORTH — LOCAL WORTHY AND POET — DIED SEVENTEEN SIXTY.

AND HERE LIES HANNAH HOLMES. WASN'T SHE A WITCH?

THAT'S RIGHT — AND BURNT IN THE TOWN SQUARE! SHE DIED SCREAMING, "I'LL GET EVEN YET!"

HER STONE'S SHAPED LIKE A WITCH'S HAT! OOH, ISN'T IT CREEPY?

WHEN MY BROTHER GETS TO PARLIAMENT, HE'S GOING TO HELP THE TOWNSFOLK — NOT CURSE THEM, HANNAH HOLMES! YOU CAN'T CURSE THEM, ANYWAY, NOW YOU'RE DEAD!

R.I.P.
HANNAH HOLMES
burnt at the stake
December 1652

'I'll get even yet!'

OOH — I'VE TRIPPED OVER THAT OLD TREE-ROOT!

AGH!

OH, MISS, LOOK! SHARON'S FAINTED BESIDE OLD HANNAH'S HEADSTONE!

IT'S NO FAINT, HELEN. I THINK SHE'S TRIPPED AND BUMPED HER HEAD.

...ON THAT HORRID GRAVESTONE! WHAT A SPOOKY ACCIDENT!

'I'll get even yet!'

YOU'VE HAD AN ACCIDENT, SHARON — KNOCKED YOURSELF OUT!

TH-THE LAST THING I REMEMBER, WAS TRIPPING OVER A TREE-ROOT! J JUST AFTER I TOLD OFF HANNAH HOLMES, FOR WANTING TO CURSE THE TOWNSFOLK!

IT'S ALMOST AS IF SHE ENGINEERED MY ACCIDENT, BY WAY OF REVENGE! BRR — MY SHADOW'S A NASTY SHADE OF BLACK!

I'M BEING STUPID. THAT BUMP ON THE HEAD'S MAKING ME IMAGINE THINGS.

ONE OF YOU GIRLS PLEASE TAKE SHARON HOME. I THINK IT BEST SHE HAS A LIE DOWN!

I WON'T TELL JOE WHAT HAPPENED IN THE OLD CEMETRY, TODAY! HE'S GOT ENOUGH ON HIS PLATE, WHAT WITH THE ELECTION AND EVERYTHING! BUT I DO FEEL A BIT STRANGE.

Some evenings later . . .

WE'LL CANVAS ROWLEY ROAD FIRST, SHARON. WHAT A DUMP IT IS, BUT I'LL MAKE BIG IMPROVEMENTS, IF I'M ELECTED!

ROWLEY ROAD

YOU'VE GOT BIG IDEAS, JOE — I HOPE YOU MAKE IT. FOR THE TOWN'S SAKE, AS WELL AS YOURS!

...YES, I'LL VOTE FOR YOU, 'COS YOU'RE A LOCAL LAD — YOU LIVE IN ONE OF THESE DAMP HOVELS YOURSELF.

THAT WE DO, MRS. MILLAR. MY FIRST PRIORITY, WILL BE TO GET A GOVERN-MENT GRANT — TO BUILD NEW HOUSES, FOR ALL OF US!

THAT WOULD BE WONDERFUL! JUST THE THOUGHT OF A NEW HOUSE PUTS HEART IN ME AGAIN.

OH HECK! I'M SHIVERING, LIKE I'VE GOT 'FLU. AND MY SHADOW'S GONE DEEP BLACK AGAIN, OVER MRS. MILLAR!

Suddenly . . .

AGH! A WATER-PIPE'S BURST!

LOOK AT MY HALL CARPET — IT'S SOPPING WET!

I'LL HELP YOU MOP UP, JOE, YOU GET ON WITH CANVASSING...

And so, later . . .

THERE — THAT'S THAT. THE EVENING SUN SHOULD DRY THE CARPET OUT A BIT!

THANKS, SHARON — YOU'RE A GOOD LASS!

THAT SHIVERY FEELING'S BACK — AND MY SHADOW'S BLACKER THAN EVER OVER THAT WASHING POLE.

OH NO, THE WASHING POLE'S FALLING.

MY FRED'S TOMATO FRAMES!

WHAT ON EARTH'S GOING ON, SHARON?

I'LL TELL YOU WHAT'S GOING ON — YOU'VE BROUGHT ME TWO DOSES OF BAD LUCK TONIGHT — FIRST THE CARPET — AND NOW THE TOMATO FRAME! I'M NOT VOTING FOR YOU AFTER ALL, JOE BROWN!

PLEASE, MRS. MILLAR — IT'S JUST COINCIDENCE!

I'M DOING NO MORE CANVASSING TONIGHT, JUST IN CASE!

NEVER MIND, JOE — IT'S JUST ONE OF THESE QUEER BAD LUCK SPELLS. THE TIDE WILL TURN FOR YOU, YOU'LL SEE!

Sure enough, a week later...

YOUR BROTHER'S JUST GOT ME A JOB, MISS — THE FIRST I'LL HAVE HAD IN FIVE YEARS! I'LL BE VOTING FOR HIM ALL RIGHT!

THAT'S SUPER, MR. STENNING!

JOHN STENNING'S GOT DOZENS OF FRIENDS! I SHOULD GET ALL THEIR VOTES AS WELL!

YOU'LL MAKE IT TO WESTMINSTER, YET, JOE. GRANDAD WOULD'VE BEEN RIGHT PROUD!

Next morning...

I'LL BUS IT HOME, WITH THE SATURDAY SHOPPING! OH, THERE'S MR. STENNING, AGAIN.

WE MEET AGAIN, SHARON. I FEEL TEN FEET TALL THIS MORNING, THANKS TO YOUR CLEVER BROTHER.

I START MY NEW JOB ON MONDAY MORNING.

THAT'S GREAT!

OOH, NOT AGAIN! I'M SHIVERING, THOUGH IT'S A WARM, SUNNY MORNING...

...AND MY SHADOW'S TOUCHED HIM — MY BIG, BLACK, HORRIBLE SHADOW!

OOPS — THERE GOES A POTATO, LOVE, I'LL GET IT FOR YOU!

OOOH, MY KNEE!

IT'S A WEAK KNEE – BUT IT HASN'T GIVEN WAY FOR YEARS! IT TAKES AGES TO RIGHT ITSELF...

Y-YOUR NEW JOB'S UP THE SPOUT, I SUPPOSE?

ANOTHER SHARE OF JOE BROWN'S BAD LUCK, EH?

THAT'S NOT FAIR! YOU HEARD MR. STENNING SAY HIS KNEE HAD GIVEN HIM TROUBLE BEFORE!

OH YES, IT IS. YOUR BROTHER'S GOT A BAD-LUCK BADGE IN HIS LAPEL, THESE DAYS! VOTE FOR HIM, AND SOMETHING WILL HAPPEN TO YOU!

BUT JOE'S NOT TO BLAME FOR MR. STENNING'S KNEE GIVING WAY. WHY, HE ISN'T EVEN HERE!

THAT'S STRANGE – MY SHADOW'S A NORMAL GREY NOW – BUT WHENEVER IT TURNS BLACK, AND FALLS ON SOMEONE OR SOMETHING, DISASTER HAPPENS! C-COULD IT BE POSSIBLE?

IT'S NOT YOU, JOE, THAT'S BRINGING FOLK BAD LUCK – IT'S MY SHADOW! CAN THAT AWFUL WITCH HAVE PUT A CURSE ON ME – LIKE SHE THREATENED?

SINCE I BUMPED MY HEAD ON THAT WITCH'S STONE IN THE TOWN CEMETERY, MY SHADOW SOMETIMES TURNS BLACK AS EVIL – AND ANYONE IT FALLS ON, HAS BAD LUCK! C-COULD IT BE THE CURSE SHE MADE BEFORE SHE DIED?

IN CASE MY SHADOW IS CURSED, I'D BETTER STAY OUT OF THE SUN, AS MUCH AS I CAN! AT LEAST TILL JOE'S WON THE ELECTION!

CHEER UP, SIS! I KNOW I'VE BEEN LOSING SUPPORT LATELY WITH MY UN-LUCKY BREAKS, BUT IT CAN'T LAST!

IF YOU DON'T MIND, JOE, I'LL STAY HERE TODAY AND GET THE TEA READY WHEN YOU'VE DONE YOUR SPEECH.

YOU'LL DO NO SUCH THING. I WANT YOU THERE, TO BACK ME UP! C'MON, WE'LL HAVE TO GO SOON!

I-I CAN'T REFUSE. HE NEEDS ALL THE SUPPORT HE CAN GET. OH, PLEASE, DON'T LET IT BE SUNNY, IN CASE MY SHADOW MUCKS THINGS UP!

GOODY - IT'S DULL AND OVERCAST! MY SHADOW WON'T GET A **CHANCE** TO WORK ANY MISCHIEF. I DON'T MIND GOING NOW!

VOTE FOR JOE BROWN - YOUR LOCAL LAD! HE **KNOWS** WHAT LEECHESTER NEEDS!

IT'S A GREAT TURNOUT!

COME ON, SHARON. YOUR PLACE IS ON THE PLATFORM, BESIDE ME! DON'T BE BASHFUL!

IT'S NOT SHYNESS THAT'S BOTHERING ME - IT'S THE SUN! IT'S BREAKING THROUGH . . . OH, I WANT TO RUN STRAIGHT HOME AGAIN!

As Joe spoke . . .

THE SUN'S GETTING STRONGER EVERY MINUTE, AND I'M SHIVERING! THAT MEANS MY SHADOW'S STARTING ITS DIRTY WORK . . . OH, I'M SCARED TO LOOK ROUND!

MY SHADOW - IT'S FALLEN OVER THOSE PEOPLE, UNDER THE TREE - BIG, BLACK, AND **HORRIBLE!** OH, PLEASE, LET NOTHING HAPPEN TO THEM . . .

But suddenly . . .

OOOH, WATCH THAT BRANCH!

IT'S SNAPPED RIGHT OFF!

ARE YOU ALL RIGHT, MRS. BOWLER? THAT BRANCH JUST GAVE WAY, FOR NO REASON . . .

THERE **WAS** A REASON - BAD-LUCK JOE BROWN WAS SPEAKING!

IT ISN'T - IT ISN'T - IT WAS MY SHADOW!

ROOF OVER YOUR HEADS, HE SAYS? SOME OF YOU ALMOST DIDN'T HAVE A HEAD LEFT THERE, TO PUT A ROOF **OVER**! I TELL YOU JOE BROWN'S **CURSED!**

HOW **DARE** YOU SAY THAT? YOU'RE TWISTING THIS THING TO WIN VOTES FOR YOURSELF!

JOE WILL LOSE **MORE** SUPPORT NOW — AND IT'S MY SHADOW'S FAULT. OH, WHAT AM I TO DO?

Later . . .

I·IT'S THAT WITCH, JOE — SHE'S GETTING HER OWN BACK AT THE TOWNSFOLK, THROUGH MY SHADOW . . . I KNOW IT!

POPPYCOCK! I'M THE BAD LUCK SPREADER . . . AND I'LL NEVER MAKE PARLIAMENT NOW! THE SCALES ARE TIPPED FOR FRED PROUDFOOT AFTER TODAY!

. . . DON'T LET YOUR PARENTS VOTE FOR JOE BROWN, KIDS — OR THEY'LL BE DOGGED BY DISASTER!

WHAT A RAT YOU ARE, GLORIA PROUDFOOT!

SORRY, SHARON! **MY** FOLK ARE VOTING PROUDFOOT NOW! YOUR JOE'S A BAD LUCK OMEN!

HE ISN'T — HE ISN'T! IT'S MY SHADOW THAT'S CURSED — NOT JOE!

YOU'VE BEEN READING TOO MANY SPOOKY STORIES, SHARON BROWN!

THIS IS AWFUL. JOE DOESN'T BELIEVE ME · AND NEITHER DO THEY! OH · SOB · I CAN'T TAKE MUCH MORE!

SHARON · WHATEVER'S WRONG?

OH, MISS BRETT· **YOU** WERE THERE, IN THE CEMETERY . . . **YOU'LL** UNDERSTAND!

But to Sharon's dismay . . .

I'M SORRY, SHARON - BUT I CAN'T BELIEVE YOUR THEORY. IF YOU ASK ME, YOU'RE TRYING TO GET YOUR BROTHER BACK HIS VOTES!

NOBODY BELIEVES ME!

OH, STOP FEELING SORRY FOR YOURSELF, AND **DO** SOMETHING POSITIVE! I KNOW WHAT I'LL DO ·

· I'LL HAVE IT OUT WITH HANNAH HOLMES · BEG HER TO LIFT HER CURSE! IT SOUNDS DAFT, BUT ANYTHING'S WORTH A TRY!

HANNAH HOLMES burnt at the stake December 1652

I'll get even yet!

OH, PLEASE · **PLEASE,** MAKE MY SHADOW NORMAL AGAIN, 'COS IT'S RUINING MY BROTHER JOE'S CHANCES, OF EVER BEING AN M.P. I'M SORRY I GOT MAD AT YOU!

121

THAT STONE - IT'S FALLING OFF THE WALL!

OWWW - MY FOOT!

SEEMS LIKE THAT WAS YOUR WAY OF SAYING, "NO", YOU ROTTEN OLD WITCH! WELL, I'LL FIGHT YOU AND YOUR CURSE MYSELF - AND FIGHT IT HARD!

HANNAH HOLMES burnt at the stake December 1652

I'll get even yet!

I'LL GET THE BETTER OF YOU YET, HANNAH HOLMES! I'LL FIGHT TO GET JOE BACK HIS VOTES, DESPITE YOUR ROTTEN OLD CURSE - SEE?

I MUST GET THE FOLK ROOTING FOR JOE AGAIN, TO MAKE UP FOR THE DAMAGE MY SHADOW'S DONE! BUT HOW?

OOPS! JOE!

YES - LARGE AS LIFE, AND PLEASED AS PUNCH, SIS! I'VE GOT NEWS! YOU KNOW THAT DISUSED STORE IN FULTON STREET? WELL -

- I'VE PERSUADED A BIG BUSINESSMAN, FROM THE SOUTH, TO COME AND LOOK IT OVER, WITH THE VIEW TO TURNING IT INTO A FACTORY! AND THAT WOULD MEAN...

...WORK FOR LEECHESTER! OH, JOE - THAT WOULD BE A BIG VOTE CATCHER, IF YOU PULL IT OFF!

At the home of Fred Proudfoot, Joe's rival candidate...

...AND I ALSO OVERHEARD HE'S MEETING THE MAN AT THREE, ON SATURDAY!

THAT COULD COST ME THE ELECTION. GOOD WORK, GLORIA!

On Saturday. . .

WELL, THIS IS IT, SHARON. WISH ME LUCK.

I DO, JOE — WITH ALL MY HEART! HERE, YOUR TIE'S NOT STRAIGHT.

Just then. . .

IT'S GLORIA PROUDFOOT!

OH PLEASE, COME QUICKLY! DADDY'S COLLAPSED IN THE LANE!

I-I CAN HARDLY BREATHE!

TAKE IT EASY, MR PROUDFOOT!

HE DOESN'T LOOK TOO BAD A COLOUR! I'VE A NASTY FEELING ABOUT THIS!

I HOPE YOUR BROTHER WASN'T GOING ANYWHERE SPECIAL, SHARON!

LEAN ON ME, AND I'LL HELP YOU INDOORS!

AS A MATTER OF FACT, HE WAS — BUT NOT TO WORRY!

I'LL MEET THE MAN FOR YOU, JOE. I CAN MAKE IT IF I RUN LIKE MAD!

NOW'S THE CHANCE I'VE BEEN WAITING FOR, TO MAKE UP FOR MY NASTY SHADOW'S WORK!

STREET

GLORIA WAS FUMING, WHEN SHE HEARD ME OFFER TO STAND IN FOR JOE! IT CONFIRMS MY SUSPICIONS THAT THE PROUDFOOTS WERE PUTTING IT ON! AH, THAT'LL BE MR DANSWORTH'S CAR DRAWING UP!

I'M SHARON BROWN, JOE'S SISTER! I'M AFRAID HE'S BEEN HELD UP, SO I'VE COME TO SHOW YOU ROUND, INSTEAD! I'VE GOT THE KEYS!

FINE, MY DEAR. NO DOUBT YOU'LL DO THE HONOURS JUST AS WELL. LEAD THE WAY!

IT HASN'T BEEN USED FOR SOME YEARS — BUT IT'S SOLIDLY BUILT! IT WOULD MAKE A GOOD FACTORY. . .

UMM, IT HAS POTENTIAL —

THEN YOU'LL CONSIDER IT? OH, PLEASE SAY YOU WILL!

LET'S JUST SAY IT'S A VIABLE PROPOSITION AT THIS MOMENT IN TIME!

THAT'S GREAT — JOE WILL BE DELIGHTED. . .OH LOOK — HERE HE IS, NOW!

AND HERE'S THE SUN COMING OUT, FOR MY DRIVE BACK SOUTH!

SORRY I WAS HELD UP. . .

Suddenly, to Sharon's horror. . .

NOT TO WORRY — YOUR SISTER'S BEEN A MOST EFFICIENT GUIDE! I LIKE THE PLACE, BROWN.

OH, HECK! I'M SHIVERING, AND MY BIG BLACK SHADOW'S AT WORK AGAIN. . . OVER MR. DANSWORTH!

Next moment...

ATISHOO — ATISHOO!

NOW HE'S DOUBLED UP, COUGHING AND SNEEZING. . . MY SHADOW'S DONE IT — MY CURSED SHADOW!

ARE YOU ALL RIGHT, SIR?

ALL RIGHT? I'M COUGHING AND SHIVERING AND SNEEZING! THAT STORE MUST BE DAMP. I'LL HAVE NO FACTORY OPENING THERE! IT'D BE THE DEATH OF ME!

OH, NO! IT WAS ALL GOING SO WELL, TILL THE SUN CAME OUT AND MY SHADOW GOT BUSY!

Back home...

IT'S NOT YOUR FAULT, JOE. IT'S HANNAH HOLMES, USING MY SHADOW TO GET REVENGE!

STOP THAT RUBBISH, SHARON — IT'S ME THAT'S CURSED, IF ANYONE IS! NO-ONE WILL VOTE FOR ME, NOW!

IT BREAKS ME UP, TO SEE JOE SLUMPED THERE IN DESPAIR. HE'S EVEN TALKING ABOUT BACKING OUT OF THE ELECTION!

Later. . .

PERHAPS THERE MIGHT BE SOMETHING IN HERE TO HELP.

AH! THERE MIGHT BE SOMETHING IN THIS, ON HOW TO BREAK CURSES!

An hour later...

YES — HERE IT IS — "ONLY LOVE, STRONGER THAN A CURSE, CAN BREAK IT." BUT HOW STRONG MUST THE LOVE BE AND IN WHAT FORM?

HEY, WHAT'S THAT ROWDY RABBLE OUT IN THE HIGH STREET?

I'LL TAKE THIS BOOK, PLEASE.

SOUNDS LIKE A MARCH OF SOME SORT. MAYBE THE FOLK ARE FOR JOE AGAIN. I CAN'T WAIT TO SEE!

DON'T VOTE FOR BADLUCK BROWN. HE WILL MAKE YOUR HOUSE FALL DOWN!

DOWN WITH BROWN!

OH, NO! THE WHOLE TOWN'S AGAINST JOE — THIS MUST BE THE END!

STRONG LOVE CAN BEAT THE CURSE, IT SAYS HERE. BUT HOW CAN YOU LOVE THE TOWNSFOLK WHEN THEY'RE SCREAMING FOR JOE TO GO?

AND NOT WHEN THEY'RE ALL BACKING FRED PROUDFOOT — AN OUTSIDER WHO DOESN'T CARE A JOT FOR OUR TOWN, REALLY! THIS BOOK'S NO USE TO ME, MIGHT AS WELL HAND IT BACK!

Back home . . .

I'LL STICK ON THE TELLY, JOE!

TO DROWN THEIR SHOUTS, EH? WELL, DON'T BOTHER, I — I MIGHT AS WELL HEAR WHAT FOLK THINK OF JOE BROWN!

JOE BROWN'S A BAD-LUCK CLOWN! PROUDFOOT'S THE GUY, TO LIFT US HIGH!

OH, JOE — IT ISN'T YOUR FAULT! IT'S BECAUSE OF MY SHADOW!

YOU MEAN BECAUSE YOU FELL ON THAT GRAVE? DON'T BE DAFT, SHARON!

OH, WHAT'S THE USE, NOBODY BELIEVES ME!

Next morning . . .

POOR JOE'S RIGHT DOWN IN THE DUMPS! THE ELECTION'S NEXT WEEK, AND IT LOOKS LIKE PROUDFOOT'S GOT IT IN THE BAG! OHO — TALK OF THE DEVIL —

WHAT A LOUSY THING TO DO — TOSSING COINS TO THE MEN ON THE DOLE . . . HIM IN HIS FLASH AMERICAN CAR . . .

... AND STEALING VOTES FROM JOE, IN THE PROCESS!

S'CUSE ME, LASS! I'M VOTING FOR FRED PROUDFOOT, ALL RIGHT!

I WON'T TELL JOE WHAT I SAW PROUDFOOT DOING — HE'S SICK ENOUGH, AS IT IS! OH, THERE'S THE DOORBELL!

HECK — IT'S PROUDFOOT! WELL, WHAT DO YOU WANT?

A WORD WITH YOUR BROTHER, IF I MAY!

HE'S COME STRAIGHT FROM DISHING OUT CASH TO THE TOWNS-FOLK, JOE!

WHAT.? I DIDN'T THINK YOU'D STOOP AS LOW AS BRIBERY...

GET OUT, BEFORE I THROW YOU OUT!

WELL, WELL — I THOUGHT YOU'D BE A BETTER LOSER THAN THAT, BROWN!

HE HASN'T LOST — YET!

Then, suddenly....

THE FIRE BRIGADE — BIG BLAZE BY THE LOOK OF THINGS! I'LL SEE IF I CAN HELP.

QUITE THE GOOD SAMARITAN, ISN'T HE? LET THE FIREMEN DO THEIR OWN DIRTY WORK, I'M INDOORS FOR A CUPPA.

THIS SHOWS YOUR TRUE COLOURS! YOU DON'T CARE FOR THE PEOPLE HERE — ONLY THEIR VOTES!

IT'S THE HEDLEY'S HOUSE — ON FIRE FROM TOP TO BOTTOM!

THERE'S A WHOLE GANG OF HEDLEYS — SIX KIDS AT LEAST! LET'S HOPE THEY'VE ALL GOT OUT!

MY HARRY — HE GOT THE KIDS OUT — BUT HE'S IN THERE HIMSELF! OH, SAVE HIM, PLEASE!

IT WOULD BE SHEER MADNESS, GOING INTO THAT INFERNO...

I'LL GET HIM, MRS HEDLEY!

JOE — COME BACK! LET THE FIREMEN DO IT — THEY'VE GOT BREATHING APPARATUS!